Gardening Nude

A Common Sense Guide
To Improving Your Health and Lifestyle
By Increasing Exposure to Nature,
Cultivating a Green Mindset, and
Building a Strong Community

Shawna Lee Coronado

Published by The Casual Gardener Company
Post Office Box 358
Warrenville, IL 60555
www.thecasualgardener.com

This book is not intended to replace common sense or a doctor's advice. Most of the medical and environmental information in this book is readily available to the public by going to the library and resourcing reference material or contacting a professional. All reference information listed in the back of this book is accurate as of the publication date of this book.

This publication contains the opinions and ideas of its author. It is intended to provide helpful and informative material on the subjects addressed in the publication. It is sold with the understanding that the author and publisher are not engaged in rendering medical, health, or any other kind of personal professional services in the book. The reader should consult his or her medical, health, psychiatric or other competent professional before adopting any of the suggestions in this book or drawing inferences from it.

The author and publisher specifically disclaim all responsibility for any liability, loss, or risk, personal or otherwise, which is incurred as a consequence, directly or indirectly, of the use and application of any of the contents of this book.

Quotes in this publication have been authorized directly by the quoted expert or corporate entity, with the exception being online references available to all for public consumption. All quotes, including online references, have been thoroughly documented in the back of this book in the Reference section.

All photos in this publication are copyright © 2008 by Shawna Lee Coronado unless designated otherwise.

Cover and Interior Design—Misty Dokken
Senior Editor—Dorothy Deer
Cover and Cover Page Photography—Sheila Rutledge (*www.capturedbysheila.com*)

For information regarding special discounts for bulk purchases, please contact The Casual Gardener Company at www.thecasualgardener.com.

First edition: September 2008

Library of Congress Control Number 2007910192

International Standard Book Number 978-0-9815733-0-4

Printed in the United States of America

The Casual Gardener Company is committed to the sustainability of the earth's resources, and in that spirit is delighted to print *Gardening Nude* on paper stocks certified by the Forest Stewardship Council (FSC). This publication has been printed by an FSC-certified printer.

FSC's mission is to promote environmentally appropriate, socially beneficial and economically viable management of the world's forests. FSC-certified stocks follow a rigorous chain-of-custody protocol to ensure that wood products such as paper come from well-managed forests or from recycled previously-used papers that meet those standards.

To Luis Coronado;
my loving husband and best friend

---

*"There are few nudities so objectionable
as the naked truth"*

—AGNES REPPLIER

The Naked Contents

Chapter One

What Is "Gardening Nude"?

∞

Gardening Nude is the answer for better mental and physical health—it is combining healthier lifestyle practices, a green conservation plan, and improving relationships through community.

Gardening Nude is a metaphor which describes a more satisfying way of life. It is discovering your naked truth and doing something with it to help make a difference for yourself and humanity.

Gardening Nude is getting out in nature (while remaining fully clothed) to strip away the excuses, the emotional baggage, and the stress by improving your lifestyle and living healthier.

Following the *Get Your Green On Healthy Philosophy* will enable you to be less stressed, improve your mood, and be healthier. You will learn how to feel better everyday by discovering, through surprisingly easy methods, that building a healthier lifestyle will lead you to a fuller, richer life filled with more satisfaction and happiness. What really defines the term "gardening nude" is the state you achieve when you get in touch with yourself, your environment, and your community.

Here's a truth: Americans are obsessed with "happiness." Most feel, if they lose more weight, look more attractive, buy more and own more, then they will be happy. Yet, consistently, this myth is debunked—happiness is not achieved by materialism. It is achieved by being self-satisfied. Obtaining self-satisfaction involves being emotionally healthy. Therefore, achieving a better mindset and living a healthier lifestyle will help you make your own happiness.

Our society has become physically unhealthy. The U.S. Health and Human Services puts out a yearly publication called *Health, United States*. The 2006 version of this study found more than 67 percent of all adult Americans are overweight, with nearly half of that number designated "obese." This is the highest number ever recorded. Obesity is caused by many factors, such as stress and poor lifestyle choices; and leads to life-threatening conditions, such as diabetes and heart disease. According to the 2007 version of *Health, United States*, heart disease is *the number one killer* of Americans for both men and women.

Our society is emotionally unhealthy. Listed in the 2006 version of this same publication is a shocking truth—the largest number of physical office and hospital outpatient visits occurs for working men and women age eighteen to forty-five. Over 200 million visits per year! Out of these visits in the years 2003 and 2004, the most frequently prescribed drug type for all outpatient visits was the antidepressant. Yet according to this very same study, only a small percentage of Americans report severe psychological distress.

For some people with truly severe psychological disorders and stress-related illnesses like diabetes, depression and heart disease, medication can be a partial, yet critical, solution. It seems clear that too many seek medication as the only solution. Why are so many people unhappy with the life they are living and seeking pills to solve their problems? Could it be that by improving our lifestyle practices, we can also improve our emotional mindset and happiness level? I say yes! I want to inspire you to feel better about yourself and about the world around you with this book. Pills are not the only solution.

Pill popping addresses symptoms, such as stress and depression, yet does not cure the infirmity. To heal yourself and our world, you must attack the problem—an unhealthy lifestyle—and help the *whole* person become healthy. By following the ideas in this book you will also contribute to better environmental practices—making the world healthier too.

By "gardening nude," I am asking my readers to stop making excuses! It is time to wake up to reality and face the shocking and naked truth: *you are the only person responsible for your happiness!*

I Never Promised You A Rose Garden

For me, gardening nude and practicing the *Get Your Green On Healthy Philosophy* has been a *miracle cure* for an unhealthy way of life. I wanted to feel better and I made it happen. Grandma Moses said it best, "Life is what we make it, always has been, always will be." You need to know, right up front, that like Grandma Moses, you also have to *want* to live a healthier life and take action to make it happen. Action is the solution, and this book is written to spur you into that healthier solution.

Most of my life I struggled to lead a healthy life. When I started practicing my healthy philosophy, over five years ago, I finally began to feel more energetic, more satisfied, and yes, happier. I have learned that being healthy means you practice all things in moderation and you do not slip back into old patterns. You must keep moving forward; when I slipped back into negative patterns, it left me devastated physically and emotionally. If you continually practice the "all things in moderation theory," it is easy to take a break without feeling as if you have fallen so far off the plan you cannot return.

With that in mind, you must understand that an instant cure for life which is 100 percent "no work" is non-existent. Everything in life worth having—*everything*—takes dedication. There is no pill that will make you permanently lose weight, cure depression, boost your energy, or cure the dozens of other things which might be wrong with your lifestyle, with the natural environment, or with society.

You must learn how to become satisfied, and this book will help show you the possibilities. It is possible to learn if you focus on living a more mindful lifestyle where you contribute to society in a positive way. Life is filled with thorns and difficulty; finding a way to survive the stress life hands you helps you get past the thorns so you can smell the roses. This is what I have learned by following my healthy philosophy. I have learned how to find more energy, be less stressed, and enjoy more contentment.

I am sure you have heard the expression, "I had to hit bottom before I could make a change." Do you believe it is true for your life? It was true for mine. I wanted that instant gratification cure so badly—the one which is non-existent—that I spiraled into an unhealthy lifestyle. I believed that a pill could heal me. My doctors would cure me and find a way to miraculously improve my stress, my health, and my mood swings even though I was not willing to do anything in my power to improve my own health practices except take a pill. After all, this is the twenty-first century. If the medical world can unlock DNA, surely they can cure a few health problems, right?

Persisting in this belief long past the time when I should have, stress combined with my negative health progression caused me, ultimately, to crash at rock bottom. By the time I got there, I was angry, self-destructive, frustrated, and held the stress of the world on my shoulders. This might be where you are right now, or perhaps you are reading this book because you see the importance of maintaining your health. With the positive energy you create by keeping optimistic and feeling self-satisfied in your life, you can give goodness to yourself, to your family, and to the world.

What I finally realized is that the experts, both medical and alternative health and wellness practitioners, cannot heal us all by themselves. These experts are intelligent, resourceful people who can point us in the right direction so that we can take control ourselves; they are not gods. They cannot touch our foreheads and zap a miracle cure into our lives. They can prescribe medications for our illnesses and suggest positive diet and exercise routines. They can warn us when the stress and unhealthy lifestyles are leading to devastation. They can perform what seems like miraculous surgeries with modern tools. These are all wonderful skills on which we now depend. In reality, however, you must address *your* side of better health. Let me cite a perfect example. Recently, I had the opportunity to speak with a friend about her lifestyle. She's curious about why I have been feeling and looking better lately; she knows my health has not always been good. My friend Stacey (her name and a few facts are changed to protect her privacy) is searching for an answer for her long-term health struggle combined with a very stressful life. Her story is the same one I hear over and over again.

"So lay it on me, Ms. Green Queen!" Stacey smiles, "Why do you look and feel so great? What's the big secret? I want to understand this whole gardening thing."

"Gardening nude is not about gardening; it's about living a greener, healthier life. Understanding where you are with your health at this moment is the first step. Right now," I say, "what is your deepest concern in your life?"

She answers thoughtfully, "I suppose it is my health. I am keeping my blood pressure and diabetes in control with medications the doctors prescribed, yet I still don't feel well. I know I'm overweight, and that influences my illness. I also have four kids, a husband, a mother-in-law, a dog, and a cat to take care of at home, not to mention a job that is difficult to say the least. How can I address my health when I can barely survive everyday at the pace I have to live? I see four doctors; one family practitioner and three specialists for my various conditions."

"Okay," I say. "What do you say to your doctors when you go in on for a typical visit?"

Stacey says, "The usual. They examine me, then I tell them my symptoms, and they give me a pill or a therapy to fix the problem. Their diagnoses all seem accurate at the time. I like my doctors, but feel frustrated that they aren't able to do their job and fix me up. Even my therapist doesn't give me a solution for why I'm feeling the way I am. I've started taking antidepressants on top of my other medications hoping that will help me cope with the overwhelming pace of it all; but nothing is working. I am beginning to understand that they might not be able to make me feel better physically or emotionally."

Stacey is right! The doctors cannot make her feel better. It is not exclusively their fault that she is not recovering. Stacey is responsible for assisting in her own healing and her own happiness. Stacey goes to several doctors, but does not make sure they communicate with each other. Therefore, they are unaware of her multiple symptoms and various prescriptions. In other words, doctors cannot understand what medical procedures might help if they are not informed more accurately of your WHOLE lifestyle.

Through my own health experiences, I have learned that doctors depend on me to focus on healthier practices at home and to guide them when a treatment is not working. I must ask for total care and demand that they speak with each other. They are now cognizant of all my medications, my activities, my stress level—everything in my life.

Form a plan with your doctors for better health and actively pursue it. By studying the *Get Your Green On Healthy Philosophy* and practicing some of the healthy habits I have listed within the plan you will be off to a good start. Soon you will start feeling better so you can be the person you want to be—more satisfied, healthier and happier.

Mind Over Matter

Physical health and emotional health are very closely linked. Frequently, people have unrealistic expectations in relationship to their emotional health. Because of popular media, they often associate it with their physical attributes, such as size and weight. One woman I met is severely depressed because she can not obtain her former eighteen year old figure through dieting. She feels that if she can reach that weight, she will attain happiness. In truth, happiness does not come from being a certain weight. Once she obtains that weight, will she *really* be happier? She will be thinner, but she will still have all the stressful emotional problems she had before. Being thinner does not mean you are emotionally or physically healthier.

When I have been stressed the most, my health suffered tremendously. I did not gain weight; I lost weight. Take it from me—being as thin as a skeleton does not make you happier. If you are overweight, losing unhealthy pounds can be fantastic for your self-esteem. In truth, however, you must solve the emotional issues which made you heavy in the first place to find self-satisfaction.

Exercise is also an important key to good health. Many people boost their energy levels by exercising. Being out in nature and breathing fresh air is important for the same reason. Remember, though, the only thing which can give you long-term happiness is being satisfied with who you are and the life you lead. That means you must address the emotional problems hidden inside your mind. Exercise can help you cope with emotional issues as much as physical issues in your life. If you can improve the emotional aspect of your life, then better health and improved body weight will follow.

What is your issue? Are you avoiding good health? Can you answer the difficult questions of why? Why are you gaining weight? Why are you stressed? Why are you depressed? You must discover whatever it is that is causing you to feel the by-products of stress which are the unhealthy symptoms. If you cannot figure it out, then ask a professional to help you to address those issues and start working them out together.

Let's get back to Stacey and our conversation. I ask her a few more questions, now focused on her emotional health. "You've been seeing a therapist. That's a great way to learn about your feelings and how to work on the emotional issues in your life."

"Yes, I feel unhappy in life. I love my family; but the poor health issues, long work hours and intense stress weigh heavily on me. My parents and extended family live far away and even with all the people I am around at work all day, I still feel very lonely. I guess I'm a little depressed, but I've found that antidepressants make me feel too far removed from life. I wander around in a daze and feel numb. I don't like that feeling either," Stacey says.

I tell Stacey, "You are stressed and isolated. I'm sure that affect's your health because stress depletes your immune system and makes your body susceptible to illness. When I was a kid we ran outside and played a lot with our friends—I had loads of energy and felt great most all the time. We gave each other support and time to enjoy the world. The reason I feel and look better is because I have recaptured that same type of energy. Of course, you cannot turn back time to be younger, but you can feel significantly better. My philosophy suggests that the feel good energy you had as a child is possible by having more exposure to nature and the environment."

I go on to tell Stacey about how the brain produces chemicals, like serotonin, which stimulate "feel good" reactions in our systems when we are exposed to sunlight. I explain, "That's why, on a gorgeous summer day you feel that natural 'high' when you step outside to run your errands."

"It's true," Stacey says, "that I rarely get outside anymore. I work. I come home. I work more. If I get lucky I watch some TV. That's about it."

Shawna and friends from the community working outdoors together to plant a public garden.

This is the truth for hundreds of Americans. Stacey is living a life filled with stress and has removed herself from the natural world. She lives in an artificial world filled with non-stop work. Who would be happy in that circumstance?

To counteract my own daily stresses, I go outside and get daylight exposure nearly every day. Going out in nature and the environment regularly, like we did when we were kids, really improves mood and energy levels. Extreme weather sometimes prevents this, but for the most part, if I am not gardening or walking outside, I still make an effort to be exposed to daylight. This lifts my mood significantly.

I discovered I feel better more often during the summer season. Being outdoors more in the summer improves my mood and can even reduce my blood pressure. After I researched this with my medical doctors, I found out about the serotonin link. I do not take antidepressants. I feel fantastic and, of course, I still have stress in my life. It is learning how to manage that stress which seems to be the key to personal satisfaction and is what my philosophy teaches. By being out in the environment moving, breathing and working, you are retraining your body to enjoy physical activity. There are hundreds of things you can do outside, from tending the roses, to building an outdoor project, to simply walking regularly.

One of my concerns about my friend Stacey is that her extended family lives hundreds of miles away. She does live with her immediate family, yet rarely sees them due to long work hours. All her children have TV's in their rooms, so they do not spend even the bare minimum of quality time together. They are hidden away in bedrooms watching TV and playing computer games by themselves in the evening. This is isolationism, and typical of many American families today.

Human beings are social creatures. Emotional connections with other people help the brain function correctly. According to Simon N. Young, Ph.D., Editor-in-chief of the *Journal of Psychiatry and Neuroscience*, "Low social support is associated with higher levels of stress, depression, dysthymia and posttraumatic stress disorder and with increased morbidity and mortality from a host of medical illnesses." That means, when we feel close to others, we are more secure with ourselves. This is due, partially, because of the increased serotonin levels which occur in these situations. Human beings need hugs, touch, and massage to encourage the brain to build connections formed on security and confidence. Giving to the community and building stronger connections also helps humans feel better and more included. Living in isolation can be stressful and, for many, it is extremely depressing. The family support unit is beginning to disappear in the United States, community ties are waning, and the stress on the human body of living in isolation is both physically and emotionally detrimental.

You can improve health significantly by rebuilding connections with people, both within family and the larger community. It is an on going effort, and it has been an emotionally rewarding thing for me to have in my life. Start with the family living in your own home. Rebuild that family community. Then take your children and your family and expand your connections by building more community within your neighborhood. Make connections. Go beyond your neighborhood. Make friends at a church, a garden club or an organization which gives back to the community. Do things which will help you reach out and touch others physically. Can you imagine how much better you would feel everyday if you had more hugs and more support and more people who really care about you?

Giving of yourself is important too, particularly when you are helping others directly. This is why, in my opinion, women live longer than men. According to the 2007 *Department of Health and Human Services Chartbook*, life expectancy in 2004 from birth was 77.8 years. In 2004, life expectancy for U.S. women was 5.2 years longer than men. Researchers predict that soon women will be outliving men all over the world.

Why? No one can definitively answer this question with proof. My feeling is because women are more likely to be caregivers who give generously of their time to take care of others. Yes, I know that evolution and genetics plays a part in this and many men are wonderful caregivers. We are looking at the majority, and universally, women play this role more frequently than men. Some scientists suggest that it is more about molecular biology than a social aspect, and there may be truth to this.

However, let's look at the fact that women all over the world are more likely to be caregivers. They are primarily responsible for building family and community. The average woman delves out a lot of physical affection—cleaning, grooming, feeding, and hugging other family members as well as helping with community outside the home. Dr. Richard O'Connor suggests in his book, *Undoing Perpetual Stress*, that stress-related trauma can physically damage the human brain. He also says that the human brain can heal itself by relearning—building new pathways for the messages we transmit. This relearning, which can happen during therapy or by living a more mindful life, is what I believe happens when we build close physical and emotional relationships within our communities. We are healing ourselves physically and emotionally.

After I told Stacey that, she sat quietly for a long time sipping her coffee and thinking. Finally, she said, "I'm shocked. I mean—I have never thought about it before, but really I've been living my life totally in isolation. My husband and I rarely talk, let alone have intimate relations or laugh." Stacey pauses, "I can't remember the last time I've had a belly laugh. I can't remember the last time I even looked into his eyes. I cannot remember the last time I really 'touched' nature or spent time appreciating a nice day. We are all too busy. I practically live at my work which is a world filled with recirculated air and artificial light. It's true that I overeat, frequently for comfort more than nutrition. I have very few friends and they are mostly related to work. I'm just too busy and now this has led me to walk a physically unhealthy path."

I smile at her as I respond, "Everyone seems too busy. Imagine a world filled with people who are too busy and too stressed and too ill to stop and talk to one another? It exists in our society today. No wonder we have diagnosed a condition called 'road rage'! Everyone says society is going to hell in a hand basket, right? Well, I believe there is one big reason—people are not spending enough time touching other human beings, people seem to not really care any more. If our society spent more time mindfully caring and generously giving, to nature and to each other, we might start to see some monumental changes in our world for the positive. People would also start feeling better about themselves and the world around them. Caring is key! The result would be better health and longer life."

The health results of caring for others can be seen in other ways too. It is a scientific fact that it is good for your emotional health to care for a pet. That is why animals are now brought regularly to hospitals and nursing homes across the United States—to help people feel better and heal emotionally. It is the effort of spending time nurturing and caring. I get a similar feeling when I do something giving for nature. When I am out in my garden digging, touching the Earth, planting, and all the things that go along with it I feel wonderful.

Undoubtedly, this great energy rush is a result of being exposed to daylight. It encourages a surge of serotonin and other feel-good chemicals to leap through the brain. I also receive positive energy knowing that the things I do which are "green" and conservation oriented are better for the people in my community. Feeling better is easy when I am gardening, recycling, and conserving. The lower garbage and utility bills are a nice side-effect of my "green" actions as well. When you are being environmentally conscious, you are *caring and giving* to our Earth—just like all those other people out there in the world who are caregivers and who are living longer and feeling better about themselves. Caring for the earth, caring for your health, and caring for and building community—*THIS* is the beginning of what "gardening nude" means.

It is also about extending that generosity to the community. Starting with the family, and spanning out to touch more people in the world. In my opinion, gardening nude is practicing "whole world health." Gardening nude is a metaphoric phrase which means combining health, conservation, and community to build a healthier lifestyle. This enables you to be physically AND emotionally healthier.

Chapter Two

Get Your Green On Healthy Philosophy

∞

The first step to "Gardening Nude" and living a more satisfying lifestyle is to follow the *Get Your Green On Healthy Philosophy*! It teaches you a new way of living. It has been my healthy lifestyle miracle which has also helped me see how I fit into the world and larger community. This philosophy is easy to understand and has helped me feel whole and complete, more satisfied in my life. It can help you, too!

Three Components To The Philosophy

The philosophy is simple and is built on my own experience over many years. This guide to improve your health and green the environment is built on a three part system which includes the Go Green Health Plan, Simple Conservation Plan and Building Community Plan. In my opinion, all are *vital* for improved mental and physical health!

When I get outdoors and work in nature I feel better—not a little better—a lot better, both mentally and physically. Ultimately, by developing and following the *Get Your Green On Healthy Philosophy*, I learned how to turn around my poor mental and physical health practices which I had been trapped in for twenty years. Applying the philosophy to my life helped me create a pattern of repeated healthy habits. When I began to follow the philosophy—and understand the systemic connection of mental health, physical health, and the environment—I soon discovered a vitality I had never experienced before.

Research confirmed by medical and psychological professionals helped solve the mystery: *Why* was I feeling *so much better* during the garden season? What was catapulting my high blood pressure back to nearly normal? What was energizing me and making me feel stronger?

Part of the answer is in the *Go Green Health Plan*. One result of following the plan is a combination of less emotional stress and improved brain chemical activity. This has been amazing for me both emotionally and physically and has *changed my life*. I have more energy, use less medication, and feel better than I ever have. If I can feel like this, so can you!

The *Simple Conservation Plan* is another part of the answer to improved health, as it encourages greener activities. Touching nature and the outdoors is an important part of my philosophy. The Simple Conservation Plan is a common-sense guide to improved greening. It also saves money by reducing your utility bills and improving your home value, while doing the right thing for the environment.

Helping The Community is another of the important items in the *Get Your Green On Healthy Philosophy*. Spending time volunteering and working with others in the community helps build emotionally satisfying relationships while you are doing something good for the Earth. This improves your mental outlook and you immediately feel better about yourself and your world.

These basic components in the *Get Your Green On Healthy Philosophy* can point you to a healthier lifestyle. Simply stated, it has felt like a "miracle cure" for me. Perhaps it will be for you, too. I want you to feel healthy, look healthy and *be* healthy so you can live a life with less stress, depression and pressure.

Years of Pain and Illness—My Personal Journey—The Story of How and Why I Discovered and Developed the *Get Your Green On Healthy Philosophy*

The road to the *Get Your Green On Healthy Philosophy* is long and personal, spanning more than twenty years, and has been filled with trial and error. This chapter explains my past unhealthy life and how I decided to make the decision to alter my lifestyle permanently. Many of you have similar stories—personal journeys filled with life's hard knocks. To alter your lifestyle for the better, you have to be ready to make a change. My goal is to inspire you with my concepts so you can start making those changes and living a better lifestyle. You will see that, like many of you, life has not been perfect or rosy for me; yet if I can feel good, be less stressed, and live better now, *so can you*!

My story begins when I was a young child in Kokomo, Indiana. We had a complicated family. I escaped from the complexities of that childhood by running free on my grandparents' farms and playing outside from dawn until dusk in our neighborhood. I loved exploring nature. Spending time lying on my back in the cool grass to watch the fluffy white clouds drift by was common place for me. At the end of the day when my Dad would whistle for me, I would come home sweaty, hungry and dirty, with a grin on my face and cuts and bruises from head to toe. It was emotionally healthy and

My father and I together at my Grandma Mabel's farm when I was two.

My parents, Don and Linda, before Dad's battle with cancer began.

revitalizing. This experience is something children today are often missing—the healing touch of nature in their lives. Physically touching the environment—learning, playing, and getting messy in nature—was good for me. It helped me heal from the painful family and social issues which our society places on children. As a child, being in nature made me feel "right," and later in life, as an adult, the scarcity of nature and environmental interaction had a strong negative effect on my health.

My dad died at age 47 of pancreatic cancer. At the time, I was thirteen years old, a moody teen, and I thought I would never survive. Every girl sees her father as the source of strength in her life; the protector and the rock of the family. I was no different. Dad was a very hard worker and a strong personality. Some called him a workaholic, but through his influence I learned that hard work is good for the soul. He taught me prior to his death that adversity should not breed laziness.

After my dad's death, I found it difficult to cope. School became a distraction instead of a focus and I did not think straight or function well for a time. My mother, Linda, was often away from the home as she now had to work longer hours to try and support the family farm on one income.

Subconsciously, I turned to the outdoors. We lived in the country at that time, near my grandparents' farm. It was good that I spent long hours outside in nature. Exploring the old barns, which smelled of hay and dirt and old tractors, and walking the cornfields, barefoot; feeling the hard dirt between my toes. My adventures included climbing trees, fences, and most everything a young girl could climb. Mowing and weeding a nearly two-acre lawn was a part of my weekly chores. Wandering through green fields among the cows and their calves, I often sang to myself and imagined all kinds of escapades. It was easy to find time to do nothing but sit in the curve of an old maple tree and listen to the wind. I explored. I healed. I grew. Later in life I looked back to that time as important and special to me. The significance of this experience did not strike me until recent years.

At seventeen, life changed even more for me—I graduated from high school and immediately moved to Chicagoland, more than three hours away from family, friends, and the open fields and farmland where I grew up. Weighing about 120 pounds, I was healthy physically. Reality quickly set in—moving away from home was not all that glamorous. Before my eighteenth birthday, I moved in with three girls sharing a tiny bedroom in a busy suburb of Chicago and began my career in business. My prime diet was boxed macaroni and cheese three meals a day as it was all I could afford. Dreams of food peppered my thoughts. My grandma's chicken noodles and country roasts were often on my mind.

Determined to succeed, I worked long hours and gradually moved up the corporate ladder. However, my personal life was a disaster. Without my familial support network, I seemed lost and felt tremendously lonely. The long hours and constant work often left me frustrated and stressed. My health suffered because I had isolated myself due to my excessive work hours, and rarely had exposure to nature. Roommates came and went, and eventually I fell into a horribly verbally and physically abusive relationship with a violent man. Sadly, I felt I had no one else and stayed in the relationship because of loneliness. No matter how miserable I was, I refused to move back to Indiana and admit defeat to my family. My father raised me to have a back-bone and I did not want the family to see me as a failure.

Here I am in my senior photo at age seventeen.

Finally I escaped the relationship after I had been severely beat, going into hiding away from the suburbs to find anonymity in the masses in Chicago. It was a gutsy move for me to make at the time as I was still under the age of twenty-one. To escape the trauma I was going through seemed unimaginable. This was the first I noticed that my stress levels were affecting my health. I found myself ill more frequently in the spring and fall with upper respiratory illnesses. In fact, I was ill, off and on year round, with constant sinus infections, bacterial infections, and bronchitis. Also, I often had yeast infections and suffered symptoms related to endometriosis. More often than not I was in physical pain. Excruciating pain would radiate from my abdomen, my back, and most often my head and face.

The doctors diagnosed a variety of illnesses based on my symptoms and prescribed pills to correct it; but I never really felt better. Living and working "in hiding" took its toll financially as well. Even though I worked long hours, the cost of living was much higher downtown Chicago and my income was insufficient to provide healthy meals. Therefore, I did not eat, exercise, or take vitamins like I should have even though my body was screaming for help.

What is Happiness?

By all outward appearances, I was confident, assertive, and growing in my work, yet I was not happy. No one knew I was struggling with my health and an oppressive, all-consuming loneliness. Dating was also confusing in my unhealthy state. Although I did not get into an abusive relationship ever again, my relationships at that time were less than perfect. Ultimately, I met and married a man who was not a good fit for me on an emotional level. We did have a beautiful daughter together and moved out of a tiny apartment in Chicago and into a second-floor condominium farther out in the suburbs. I rarely spent time outdoors.

During the next four years I continually struggled to find what I felt was happiness. Defining happiness became difficult. By now my career had expanded and I opened a small art and design firm. When I received my first order to paint a flower, I sat for hours trying to think of what a real flower looked like. When I was a child, I worked in the garden with one of my grandmothers, she had flowers. I thought and thought and could not remember the last time I had seen a flower growing in nature. It had been nine years since I moved away from Indiana and it occurred to me that I felt withdrawn from nature. To research flowers, I ordered dozens of flower and perennial catalogs. I studied every flower in each catalog carefully, remembering the Latin name, the angle of the leaves, the stem, and the look of the plant. It became clear that I was addicted to learning about horticulture. Very soon thereafter, the Chicago Botanical Gardens became my favorite place to take my daughter and her friends. Often we wandered the grounds just for the peace of it. Without realizing it, I was craving nature and trying to rediscover a place where I could feel good again. Studying horticulture and the environment became a passion. Plant science fascinated me, and I began balcony gardening at home. Creating commercial floral art became my design specialty.

Balancing life and career continued to be a struggle. Perhaps because of my influences as a child, I have always felt driven when working. For me, I derive satisfaction from doing a job the correct way the first time. Therefore, I threw myself into my new business and worked hard to get it off the ground. Night hours were normal at my home office. I often worked until 2:00 AM filling orders and up again at 6:00 AM to take care of my daughter. My husband worked during the day while I watched our little girl. Under the on-going stress, my health started acting up as it had in the past. Finally, my doctor ordered surgery for endometriosis.

While convalescing, I realized my marriage was failing much like my health. My husband and I rarely spent any quality time together, both because of our long work hours and the personality mismatch. I felt more stressed, lonely and unhappy than ever. It drove me to desperate and unhealthy measures. Depressed and lonely, I sank to an all-time low. I turned inward and became self-destructive. It was a dark time for me. My health, from both an emotional and physical aspect, was very poor. Our marriage ended and with it went the tiny support network I had.

After my daughter and I got out on our own, I began to think more clearly and build a life-plan we could live by. Maintaining possession of my home and providing food for the two of us became a difficult struggle. Because my daughter was not old enough for

Here's a photo of my daughter and I when we started life over again.

full-time school, I maintained a variety of part-time jobs where she was allowed to come along, they included scrubbing laundry, painting, cleaning houses, mowing lawns, childcare and data processing. When my daughter spent time with her father, I waitressed, pulling double shifts and collapsing in exhaustion when she returned. Although I gave up the commercial art business because it did not bring in enough money to support my home, I still filled small custom art orders. This was the work I loved, and often I would stay up until the early morning hours working on these projects. It was difficult, and for a short time became even more emotionally and physically exhausted trying to keep everything together.

When my daughter turned school age it was time for a full-time job and I started a career in the technical sales field. Driven to succeed, I stayed in the technical industry off and on for several years reaping a good salary, although, again, working long days. Spending more time with my daughter and throwing myself into work became an important source of dissipating the self-destructive pattern I had fallen into. I dated some, but ended anything that became "serious," as I knew I was not ready for a relationship that would tap into previous negative patterns. It seemed clear to me—my daughter and I needed to take time to heal. At that moment, it meant leaving any intimate relationships behind so I could focus on creating a positive self-image, a stronger financial base, and raising my young daughter. Slowly my life was changing for the better.

By now I had been diagnosed with allergies, although I had not been officially tested yet. I was at one doctor or another several times a month and was in constant pain from sinus pressure. I learned that molds were my strongest trigger. Eliminating mold foods from my diet helped, but did not eliminate allergies entirely. I stopped eating cheese, yeast breads, beer, wine and mushrooms; and I still maintain those restrictions today as much as possible.

Although I started feeling a little better, the stress of the divorce and the confusion I had over my diet and my health made my weight plummet. One day I looked in the mirror and realized the image looking back at me was like a skeleton. At 5'4" tall, I weighed only ninety-five pounds and was continuing to lose the weight. I avoided mirrors and having photos taken, I felt weak. Although I was improving my mental and emotional mindset, stress was really harming my health. I started having aches and pains regularly where I had never had them before. My back frequently "went out" and I was left with the inability to walk for a week or so at a time. Because of this, I was on regular pain medication. Doctors gave me pills for pain, pills for allergies, and pills to cure the side effects of the pills.

A Breakthrough

When I could, I spent more time outside and really enjoyed it. From an emotional level, my daughter and I had developed a wonderful relationship. I was beginning to feel better about our life and the positive direction in which we .were moving. Work was good, although stress was always a burden. We spent more time outdoors and I gained confidence realizing through hard work and faith in myself, I could live better and give my daughter a better life too.

The allergy problems continued through the years and I felt as if I would never be without either a sinus infection or bronchitis. Sensitivity to smells was also becoming a serious issue, particularly chemical odors. A significant change in my treatment began when I started *talking* to my doctors. Asking questions and pressuring them for responses which made sense to me became a priority because I could no longer tolerate living in poor health. For the first time, I realized that you have to work *with* your doctors. They are not gods—they can only treat the symptoms if you are willing to help them find the cause and participate dually in a relationship to improve your health.

The doctor who helped me the most has been Nirmala Arora, M.D., an allergy specialist who was, and still is, tremendously patient with me. My allergies were extreme and I was taking more than a dozen medications a day simply to survive. I could not breathe well, my face was constantly clogged and in pain due to upper respiratory symptoms. Sleeping regularly became impossible. My body was so sensitive I would frequently have negative reactions to the prescribed medications.

It was Dr. Arora who turned to me one day and said forcefully, "Shawna, this has to end! We are treating your symptoms; we are not treating the problem! We must discover what is causing this!"

Dr. Arora gave me a complete battery of allergy tests. I found out I was allergic to more than molds. My allergies encompassed house dust, ragweed, bananas, melons, cats, dogs, corn, peanuts, feathers, grass, and trees. Citrus and berries would trigger a reaction, although I was not directly allergic to them. Many chemicals also gave me reactions including Paraphenylenediamine (PPD), Para-aminobenzoic acid (PABA), Sorbitol, Sulfas, and dozens of other chemicals and preservatives. I would develop rashes, cough uncontrollably, be unable to concentrate, suffer from frequent headaches, have sinus infection after sinus infection, and the list of symptoms would go on and on. My extreme sensitivity to smells increased. Once I started vomiting and fell on the ground unconscious when I was exposed to a heavy dose of ozone from an ozonator machine. My body was under attack daily due to allergies, it began to make sense why I was constantly sick. I felt relief at finally knowing the real source of the problem. Slowly, the doctor and I began working together. It took two years of going through various medications to find the right combination that worked for me.

Meanwhile, my daughter seemed healthy emotionally and my ex-husband and I were cooperating in raising her. The forward momentum of our lives started to feel different and better. Although the allergies still plagued me, my overall emotional health was coming around. And that is when it happened: I met a man who helped me discover my naked truth!

A Healthier Phase

Luis Coronado and I met during one of my sales calls. We became fast friends. Although I didn't know it at the time, his influence in encouraging me to stick with my personal health plan would ultimately change my life for the better.

A year after we started dating, Luis and I were married in a small ceremony with immediate family present. Having Luis's strong and calming force in our lives was a beautiful thing for both my daughter and I. Since I lived so far away from my family, Luis brought a huge gift to me with his. It was this family experience that really taught me how good it is to give more to community and to help others.

I was starting to gain weight and almost weighed 100 pounds in this photo, this is shortly after Luis and I started dating.

Simply by his stalwart presence, Luis forced me to think about family, friends and community. He taught me the importance of building and maintaining good relationships. Soon I felt better than I ever had on an emotional level and realized that being personally satisfied also involves leaving isolation behind to become more socially connected with the world.

My husband, Luis, is in this photo with me. You can tell how happy we are together. I have started to feel better by being outdoors in nature more with my family.

We soon became pregnant. My allergist's husband, Vipal K. Arora, M.D., S.C., is also my Obstetrics/Gynecology specialist. He discovered that along with my allergies and regular infection issues, I had gestational diabetes. The doctor sent me to a nutritionist who changed my diet even further and helped me learn to take blood samples six times a day to monitor sugar levels. Luis watched me carefully. By the eighth month of pregnancy, Luis could tell by my stress or anxiety level if I had too much sugar that day. We confirmed this sugar sensitivity regularly with my blood sample test scores.

Luis has always been a very affectionate man and we discovered during my pregnancy that massage helped reduce many of my negative symptoms. The physical contact,

I believe, had a direct impact on my brain and nervous system. It led to increased physical wellness as well as a more positive emotional state. Richard O'Connor, Ph.D., suggests in his *Undoing Perpetual Stress* that injured brain connections can be remapped by building positive relationships, particularly relationships that involve physical touch such as hugging and massage. My own experience reinforces his theory.

Of course, my daughter's loving and affectionate relationship with me contributed to better health as well. Family and community relationships helped me to heal further. Even my childhood hurts no longer seemed as critical as they always had. It became important not to hate or despise my past, but to accept it. Sharing, touch, and giving to others became a way to truly enrich my life. I started to feel more and more satisfied with who I was because of these experiences.

In a moment of personal revelation I discovered it was not important to have more "things" to help satisfy a subconscious craving for happiness, but to accept and be satisfied with the things you have. It seems so obvious now, but when I realized it, I was shocked by the revelation. Being satisfied with who you are and being secure in the environment in which you live is more significant in moving towards perceived "happiness" than anything else. Finally, the health light bulb went on: *Living a satisfied life IS being happy!*

Luis is the photographer behind the camera–this shot was taken of "the girls" at a wedding we attended. We are all healthier and happier than before.

Then an interesting thing happened after Luis and I had our baby and I stopped treatment for the gestational diabetes. Luis continued to notice my emotional mood swings would increase when I had too much sugar. I would lose the ability to concentrate and would be moody and anxious. The combination of stress and sugar increased the problem. The issue seemed connected with processed sugars versus natural sugars; however all sugar had a direct impact on my mood and my life.

Finally, we determined that sugar sometimes threw my allergic reactions to my "regular" allergens into mayhem. My face would be in pain for days and days after I ate a piece of pie. I was not allergic to the pie, but I was beginning to see how I was connected to all the food I ate as well as the natural environment. Stress increased symptoms. It soon became clear that cutting excessive processed sugar products from my diet needed to become a permanent lifestyle change. Although reducing the amount of processed sugar is part of eating a more healthy diet, this does not mean everyone needs to avoid sugars. For me, it is critical and seems to be directly connected to my systemic health.

Falling Off The Horse and Getting Back Up

Luis and I moved to a larger home where we had more access to the outdoors. The garden became my joy. When I was in the garden my stresses would diminish. Physical labor was good. I gained muscle and a healthier weight. My youngest daughter spent hours outside with me discovering and enjoying the outdoors. As the gardens expanded so did our delight, we played with worms, we examined butterflies, and *we lived in nature*.

Gardening gave me such a sense of comfort and stress relief. On the weekends I felt the best because I was outdoors more. Even with my exposure to outside allergens, I felt better and could breathe easier due to the increased exposure to sunlight. With Luis's emotional support and constant encouragement, I was "gardening nude"—it felt great to leave behind all the excuses. I was saying goodbye to the negativity, my emotional issues, my stress, and my pain. Getting

Garden rooms and walkways in Shawna's home garden.

out there allowed me to strip it all away and allow nature to heal me once again, much like it had when I was a child. As testimony to that, during the winter, when I was away from the garden, the negative symptoms would return and my blood pressure would increase.

Before I knew it, I was building more and more gardens and gaining great self-confidence and physical strength. Here are a few photos of my personal gardens. Being outdoors and creating these gardens helped me gain strength and become healthier.

Soon I became the horticultural expert for my neighbors. The garden facilitated a growing interest in my community. Helping people allowed me to learn about the environment and I begin sharing knowledge about conservation, recycling, and going green. Soon I started a gardening and greening newspaper column. Before long that soon expanded to other newspapers. In reality, I was beginning to practice the Go Green Health Plan without even knowing it was a health plan. Eating better, living better, and feeling better was possible.

Outside of gardening and family, there was still one aspect of my life that was stressful; work. I had been staying at home with the children after the baby was born. When Luis was laid off from a large technical firm, I went back to work full-time to support the family. That increased my stress and also increased my allergy conditions. Once again I was spending more and more time at the allergist for on-going issues. Often I had to be put on steroids to help counteract my upper respiratory issues. Steroids affected my personality by making me angry, stressed, and aggressive. Nonstop yeast and bacterial infections plagued me as well. The more stress, the more doctor visits.

Another health disaster that year was a flood which happened in our basement, followed by an extensive mold abatement. Our family continued to live in the house while the mold abatement went on. One day after being exposed to the catastrophe, I ended up at my doctor, unable to breathe. The heavy exposure to molds tortured me by making breathing labored and increased all my allergy symptoms. I felt so sick I could not get out of bed or escape the migraine headache reaction. This lasted for weeks. Trembling and weak, I would lie in bed and cry because I was unable to do anything else. It was, I think, the most difficult time in my life from an allergy and health perspective. Ultimately, I had a severe asthma reaction. When I saw my doctor, barely able to breathe, I broke down and cried miserably. She watched as I tried to tell her, whispering because I was unable to speak from laryngitis, that I did not understand why the world was against me. Why did I have this illness? Why did I have these allergies? How am I going to survive this?

Dr. Arora replied quite vehemently, "Shawna, life is never easy! You have to stop feeling sorry for yourself and start doing something about this or you will end up in the hospital. Start treating your body as a whole!"

It took another year for me to comprehend totally what she was saying because I was so fully entrenched emotionally and physically in trying to survive the on-going attacks. For the time being, I was placed on heavy doses of steroids along with the other allergy medications I was taking. There were now stronger and more frequent doses of asthma medicines as well. I was taking over a dozen medications per day. My medicine cabinet looked like a pharmacy.

Health-wise, that year was difficult because I felt as if I took a step back from my health plan. The flood happened at the beginning of the year, and I suffered the rest of the year with asthma and breathing issues. I

Nirmala Arora, M.D. has been Shawna's allergist and friend for over ten years. Here is a 2008 photo of Dr. Arora and Shawna.

wore a heavy ventilator mask outside while gardening. I would not give up my connection to nature because I felt it was already a critical need for my health. I decided to work around the asthma. I was determined to become healthy again.

That fall I changed jobs. I found a position that offered a better pay and benefit package, important since Luis's business did not provide health insurance and we were having increasing difficulties meeting all the doctor bills. I commuted to downtown Chicago three or four days a week and managed the rest of the work from my home office.

The new job was frustrating, primarily due to extensive work and travel hours, but the need for medical insurance was strong. I began to feel detached from my family unit since I spent so much time away from them. I felt tremendously sad that I could not garden much or spend time outside.

Once again, I started to feel ill almost constantly. I lived with back pain and allergy-related pain most of that season. One winter day I woke up and cried passionately because I could not garden and had not been home in the daylight for weeks—I left before dawn and returned after dusk. My work required more time than I thought it would, which meant I spent more and more time away from the girls and Luis. Rarely exercising, I had truly fallen off my health plan. It felt as if I was spiraling downward, with no control over my life or what was happening to my health. Depression and upset over the situation finally pushed my health over the edge. It became difficult to walk the few blocks from the train to my office in Chicago. I felt tremendously exhausted and increasingly anxious. I had no energy. Strangely, I began craving red meat and ice. I ate ice morning, noon, and night. Getting up in the morning became impossible without a monumental effort.

When I went to my gynecologist, Vipal K. Arora, M.D., S.C., for a check-up he was more than concerned. He gave me a well deserved lecture, "Are you taking vitamins? This is critical! Do you exercise? It is important that you see your body as a system. You must take care of it regularly!"

Vipal K. Arora, M.D. and Shawna in July of 2008.

He also discovered I had extremely high blood pressure. That particular day, my blood pressure was so high he would not let me leave his office until I was able to lower it. I was ordered in for immediate blood tests and sent to a practitioner who would help me reduce the blood pressure. It turned out that I was bleeding excessively during menstruation and it was creating an anemic complication. Combine the anemia diagnoses with high blood pressure and excessive stress, and my body was out of control. On top of all the medications, I also started taking high blood pressure medication and vitamins with a heavy iron concentration.

The doctor said I had two possibilities to solve the problem—a hysterectomy or endometrial ablation. The latter was a surgical procedure which stopped my monthly periods without major surgery. My blood count was low, and he told me I might have to have blood transfusions that week before the surgery. He warned me how serious this was, stating that people can die from anemia at the level I was suffering; he wanted me to have the surgery within days, not weeks. I began to panic. When I told my family what was happening and saw their faces fall, I had an intense moment of realization. It was my fault; I knew I had let my health run out of control by temporarily falling off my routine and not practicing my regular health plan. Staying on the plan would mean I would have a longer life. Without a doubt, I was heading for disaster because of stress and poor health management.

Endometrial ablation is an outpatient procedure, so I chose it as an easier solution. I remember my superior at work being upset that I missed time off the job. As soon as I recovered, I rushed back to the office and began the long hours all over again, busting the proverbial hump for more money that I felt my family needed.

One positive thing came from having anemia. I started taking vitamins, *finally*! I started eating better. Having anemia at the serious level I had really scared me and forced me to realize that I was far more responsible for my health than I ever imagined. I finally began to understand that my poor health was not just about the allergies. My doctors were shouting at me "your body is a system." I had to keep the entire system functioning. Better health encompasses both emotional health and physical health. Exercise, eating well, building community, and strengthening my relationship with the environment; better health is *all* of this.

Then a very fortunate thing happened which allowed me to make the change I needed to be healthier. My manager pulled me into her office and said she wanted me to spend more time downtown at the main office. Thinking about all the stress my family had to suffer because of this career, thinking about the hours and hours the children were without me, made the decision an easy one. The money was not worth it. Without any difficulty at all, I took a deep breath, smiled, and said, "This job is not for me!" I was led smiling out the door without packing my desk. Phoning Luis on the train ride home, I told him what happened. We did not know how we would get by financially, but living with the stress we had been suffering through was not the answer. It was time to get back that feeling I had before—the one where I was on my health plan, close to nature and close to my family, the one where I was satisfied with my life. If I could do that, then my family would be healthier too.

Over the last few years, I had been following a health plan which really helped; I had fallen out of healthier habits. Resolutely I decided to live a better life with less time away from the family. Why not dedicate myself to making my lifestyle the healthier lifestyle I envisioned? Of course, perfection is unattainable, and I knew it would be a lot of hard work, but everything worth having in life IS hard work, and it was better than living dangerously by being unhealthy.

A Happy Change

Downsizing in one's personal life is a "hip" term right now, it usually means to dispose of your current career and find another that pays less, but is more satisfactory. I decided downsizing was for me. I was frightened to live "without" what I had before, but my mother-in-law was quick to point out that the family would adjust, and that all of us would be unhappy if I continued on a career which pushed me away from them. As the saying goes, "If Mama ain't happy ain't nobody happy!" Too true! Luis was very happy in his self-made business. Perhaps I could do that too. The first year was slow going, but rewarding, as I forged ahead with a small landscape design firm.

Most importantly, my goal now was to continue to follow my "health plan" which allowed me to feel better, breathe better, and be closer to the ones I loved. Back before the mold abatement health issue, I remember feeling better than I ever had. At that time, I had connected intimately with family and with nature. The newspaper column I wrote also allowed me to connect with the community through my writing. Downsizing also meant improving the quality of my life as a whole. Because, as my doctors kept discussing with me over all these years, "your body is a system." It also means that what you eat, how you live, how you touch the environment, how you expose yourself emotionally to family and friends, how you exercise, how you do *everything* is connected to your health. My goal, now, was to be dedicated to my health plan—for my physical health and for my sanity!

Understanding clinically why I felt so much better during the "garden" season and when I was following my health plan became important. When I first went to see my high blood pressure doctor, he clearly told me that if I could learn how to meditate, I would be able to lower my blood pressure. My response, I am embarrassed to say, was that I did not believe in any of this "new-age mumbo-jumbo" and could not believe that meditation would make any difference at all. Several weeks later, after I read up on high blood pressure, I humbly came back to him with agreement and additional questions. We examined my entire history. Finally, he told me directly, "It is not only the increased exercise level, although I see that as a factor. The most likely reason you are reducing your blood pressure only during the gardening season is because of the gardening itself. It is well-known that there is a meditative quality about gardening. You have discovered this for yourself. You have lowered your blood pressure by a number of factors; by exercising, by living healthier, and because you have learned how to meditate. This is not a traditional way to meditate, but it is producing the results your body needs." Astonishing! It is not new-age mumbo-jumbo!

This was an epiphany! Excitedly, I rushed home to tell Luis, "Do you realize what this means? Gardening and being out in the environment has reduced my blood pressure. Being in touch with people also makes me less depressed and more energized. Taking vitamins and eating several smaller meals per day also makes me feel a lot better! It takes more than just one of these activities to make a person truly healthy. Why, this is common sense! This is amazing! Why isn't everyone doing this?"

He smiled, finally, I "got" it. However, I was not satisfied with just knowing the answer. It seemed important to me, that if I could do it, maybe I could inspire others to understand how to live healthier and feel great also. My new goal became researching the medical truth of what I had discovered so I could spread the message to others.

Everyday I felt a little better. Everyday I read and researched non-stop to educate myself about the truth, driving myself to find the whole answer; the naked truth. I wanted to prove to myself and to my readers that I had discovered a way for people to feel better and be healthier. In my enthusiasm, I realized that this could lead to less depression and enhance people's mindset about thinking positive. Not everyone has had the traumatic health and emotional background I have lived with, but everyone still wants to feel good everyday. We all have a certain amount of baggage we carry around, so it becomes important for everyone to strip away the excuses and just get healthy. Getting off the couch becomes impossible without facing the truth. "Gardening Nude" soon became an expression which defined a way of life I wanted to share with the world.

Doctors like David Edelberg, M.D. who wrote *"The Triple Whammy Cure"*, Richard O'Connor, Ph.D., who wrote *"Undoing Perpetual Stress"* and Andrew Weil, M.D. who wrote *"Healthy Aging"* all emphasize total body health. They speak of being mindful. They also discuss the effects of the environment on brain chemicals. Serotonin is one of the key chemicals mentioned as a "feel good chemical". It is one of the chemicals in our brain which kicks in and makes us feel wonderful on a sunny day. Many researchers confirm that direct daylight exposure with no sunglasses stimulates serotonin production.

Unfortunately brain chemicals cannot always fight stress. It will always be in a person's life, even if you work hard to eliminate some of it. Having a high-energy and "driven" spirit means stress is a part of my daily routine, proof of this came one day not to long ago when I caught a winter virus and suffered from nose bleeding, I was referred to an ear, nose and throat specialist named Dino Delicata, M.D. The doctor listened carefully to my concerns and ran a scope through my sinus regions and down my throat. He surprised me when, after the procedure, he leaned back and pronounced that I sometimes have trouble sleeping. Shocked, I said, "Why yes I do, although it's improved significantly since I've been exercising more. I can get to sleep fine, but have trouble staying asleep. I thought it was because of my dust allergies. I always wake up with my sinuses completely clogged and I am frequently in pain when that happens. How did you know?"

"It's stress!" Dr. Delicata leaned in closely and examined the taught muscles surrounding my sinus region, neck and back. "Your body does not cope well with stress. Many people act out their stress by clenching their jaw while sleeping." My history is indicative that stress largely touches my health, so this made sense. He went on to tell me about bruxism, which is a condition that happens when you clench or grind your teeth usually due to stress-related issues. Clenching means you tightly hold your top and bottom teeth together, especially the back teeth. Clenching puts pressure on the muscles, tissues, and other structures around your jaw and can cause sinus pain.

Dr. Delicata said, "Your sinus region is under pressure by two elements. First, your allergies force your face to swell at night. Second, you might be subconsciously clinching your jaw, neck, and face muscles during the day and while you sleep because of the regular stress you are under. This constant strain causes pressure on your sinus region and the tightness encourages mucous to stay in the area. It is a complicated trigger which might be enhancing your allergy symptoms and increasing the pain you feel through your sinus region." I stared at him in amazement for a full minute after he said that. Once again, I was being shown that learning to cope with stress is important and is a life-long pursuit.

The reason I am discussing this is because the experience with Dr. Delicata has convinced me more than ever that the human condition is a delicate balance. Even when I follow a healthy lifestyle plan like I do, stress can and WILL still touch my life. Catching a virus, or suffering from exhaustion, is still something that can easily happen to a healthy person. Stress is such a powerful factor in all our lives and can lead to depression, diabetes, heart disease, high blood pressure, immune system disorders, fibromyalgia, and many other conditions. Try as I might, I cannot escape stress. Neither can you. Therefore, it is important for you to live healthier and find more effective ways you and your family can cope with stress. I believe living a healthier lifestyle and gardening nude is key to this. Stripping away the excuses to get better health is one of the most important things you can do for yourself. It lays the foundation so you and your family can fight the stressful conditions you will face. Teaching your children and community how to live healthier is a legacy which is more important than any monetary or materialistic gift you can give.

That is where I am with my health today. By following the *Get Your Green On Healthy Philosophy*, I have reduced my regular allergy and high blood pressure prescriptions from over a dozen, down to only three. Stress, as Dr. Delicata pointed out, will never completely go away. It still profoundly touches my life and health. However, I no longer suffer regularly from severe asthma. I sleep better than I did one to two years ago. There are days I still feel quite ill from allergies, but it is far, far better than it ever was before because I am paying attention to my health. Walking and outdoor exercise are very important to helping me feel better. Often, I remind myself of where I was ten years ago and know that life has truly changed for me for the positive.

There is no end conclusion to my on-going health story. It is dependent on my following the health plan. I work every day to reduce my stress, eat right and live green. I do, however, consider my story one with an on-going happy outcome because I feel good. I enjoy life more, am less depressed and am healthier. I have learned how to systemically treat my body by living a healthier lifestyle.

Generally speaking, we must treat our health like the systemic animal that it is. We cannot treat it with a pill or only one solution when the body needs multiple healthy behaviors to sustain itself at an energetic level. I continue to do research to open up understanding for myself and my readers. Recognizing that being healthful *is a way of life*. It is not something that can be done partially. To have better health you must *commit to a change in your lifestyle!*

Recently I visited with Nirmala Arora, M.D. to tell her what's happened for me since I left a stressful job, did intense research on emotional and physical health improvement, started living a healthier life, and have been writing about it. I shared, to my great relief, that I am finally in touch with my allergies and practice daily exercise, eat better, and take vitamins. I shared with her the many other things I do which help me to cope better than popping pills ever did. We discussed this at length. She knows Luis and was happy to hear about the ongoing support from both his family and mine. She was excited to hear about the *Get Your Green On Healthy Philosophy* and about the message I want to spread to the world.

Dr. Arora surprised me then. She pulled me up out of the chair, hugged me, and told me how proud she was of me. In her line of work she sees so many people who never achieve this knowledge and remain perpetually sick and suffering even with her efforts to help them. She reminded me that it takes a patient's strength to work with the doctor, to ask questions, and educate the doctor by providing a complete medical accounting. It did her heart good, she said, to see me take the lead and make a difference. Both of us had tears in our eyes. Dr. Arora has traveled this road with me for over ten years and will continue to be there in the future as an intimate part of my healthy community. I will not let the allergies and poor health practices win and get the best of me any more. I am saving the best of me for my family and friends.

The amazing part of gardening nude and following the health plan I have developed is that I feel better, look better, *am better* than ever in my life. I am happy with myself, my family and I am satisfied with my life. I am able to cope better with daily stress. This is my story; I have worked hard to leave poor health behind, and I have done it by following the Go Green Health Plan, Simple Conservation Plan, and Building Community Plan— all together it is the *Get Your Green On Healthy Philosophy*. Developing and living this philosophy is what is responsible for the great way I feel today and I hope it will be responsible for inspiring you to live a healthier way of life too!

As you can see by this 2007 of Luis and I, life is good and we are doing well. I am a very strong and healthy 130 pounds in this photo and I am also the healthiest and most satisfied I have ever been. I feel much better and only take three medications per day.

Part I—
Go Green Health Plan

The best six doctors anywhere
And no one can deny it
Are sunshine, water, rest, and air
Exercise and diet.
These six will gladly you attend
If only you are willing
Your mind they'll ease
Your will they'll mend
And charge you not a shilling.

—COUNTRY NURSERY RHYME, QUOTED BY WAYNE FIELDS,
WHAT THE RIVER KNOWS, UNIVERSITY OF CHICAGO PRESS, 1990

#	O	N	#	4	#	G	O
N	%	I	N	O	&	9	O
E	N	S	B	1	+	Z	D
E	A	2	E	;	Y	%	#
R	K	!	S	6	O	8	%
G	E	T	T	4	U	?	Q
#	D	3	:	X	P	8	#
R	U	O	Y	#	T	E	G

Chapter Three

Go Green Health Plan

∞

F ollowing the Go Green Health Plan will help you feel better, look better and *be* better. The plan is simple to follow and easy to understand.

Being healthy means more than being physically fit. Being healthy is a systemic by-product of living a positive lifestyle. The health plan I have created touches on emotional and physical health in both categories. When I spoke with the community regarding my plan, I noticed they began asking the *why* questions to better understand their own lives in relation to starting a health plan, Why am I not satisfied with my life? Why am I so out of shape? Why am I not happy even though I have everything I could possibly want? Why do I feel horrible? Why am I so stressed? Why is my life miserable? To answer my readers questions of *why*, it is important to understand how people can be so miserable and unhappy in the first place.

When I began researching how people felt, I learned that almost always the answers were negative to the "Are you happy?" question. This surprised me. Many people expected to be happy in life because *they felt they deserved it*, not from setting and attaining goals for their success. Not because of hard work. And certainly not because they had worked to build their emotional and physical health. Many felt extremely depressed and filled with anxiety when they examined their lives. They realized they were not happy and could not be happy living the way they were. This applied no matter how wealthy or how poor the person might be. All of this confused me—why did people expect to be handed happiness? I learned an important lesson through this basic research—*you* are the only person responsible for your happiness! Happiness in life is based on self-satisfaction and self-acceptance of the world around you, it is not about monetary gratification. I also discovered that people who were more physically healthy and who were more in-tune with nature were often more satisfied people in general.

Why do so many people say they are not "happy" and cannot attain happiness and self-satisfaction? My idea is because people do not understand they have to take responsibility for their total health and fix it themselves. Like many people in society, I avoided making positive emotional and physical health choices for a long, long time. I was miserable and unhappy, particularly about my physical health. I wanted the doctor to fix me quickly, like a car repair expert would fix my car. Quick and easy! No problem! I did not understand that I had to take responsibility and "fix" myself!

The truth is the answer to the "whys" of happiness and self satisfaction can be found by addressing the *cause* instead of the *symptoms* of negative emotional and physical health. I fooled myself into believing that the quick cures would be long-term solutions (if only life was that convenient). When I would feel better for a time, I always ended up back at an unhealthy point, due to continuing stress and lack of proper care for my body. Ultimately, being unhealthy will catch up with you like it caught up with me. Using quick fixes cannot be the solution. It will be our society's legacy, however, if we cannot change this unhealthy pattern within our society.

Many people told me they felt miserable and overwhelmed with the lack of support from their family structure. They were so busy and so stressed with life, they felt lonely and cut off from society and this enhanced their miserable status. In my opinion, the modern family will suffer because the children are being raised by parents who live unhealthy lives and feel the quick solution is the "do all end all." Quite often, people are forced into this lifestyle simply from the cost of living. Both parents often work full time in the United States, sometimes the parents must work two jobs.

Being unhappy and miserable is a result of a combination of conditions. It is not just poor health. It is not just isolationism. It is not just lack of concern for the environment's health and how it affects you. It is *all of this* combined. I remember reading a bumper sticker that said, "The one with the most toys wins!" Comical? Yes! A keen example of materialism in modern society? Yes! It often seems as if it is all about money. We sacrifice our health so we can obtain more money and more things.

Wealthier people are not happier people. Rich young Hollywood-chic men and women are shown daily on the news flitting to parties of the wealthy "see and be seen" crowd. Paradoxically, often the same young partiers are shown after the party, miserable, depressed, suicidal, and in drug rehabilitation programs. It is a confusing societal picture for most of us to understand. Money is equal to power, but it is not equal to happiness.

A clinical psychologist and expert on family stress, Madeline Levine, Ph.D., author of *The Price of Privilege: How Parental Pressure and Material Advantage Are Creating a Generation of Disconnected and Unhappy Kids,* HarperCollins, 2006, wrote her book after she observed wealthy young preteens and teens entering her office with depression, anxiety, loneliness, and self-destructive behaviors. The problem, she believes, results from strong messages sent from parents and teachers that tell children

Madeline Levine, Ph.D. to excel and seek material success, even at the expense of healthy development. Dr. Levine describes this as "the culture of affluence." This trend is not limited to wealthy families, but to any parents who tend to value material goods over relationships and competition over cooperation. Dr. Levine says, "Common sense shows that a child's first community is their home. If they grow up believing they have a contribution to make, they'll have an easier time raising a family and being part of a community."

Children often imitate their parents. What legacy are we leaving our children if we teach them to rush through life with high materialistic goals which are unattainable? I can testify personally to this fast pace and difficult level of life. It is certainly a struggle for me to maintain a busy family schedule in our modern society. One of the most important concerns is that across the nation people are becoming isolated from social groups. Spending time with family and community, eating together, learning about nature together, giving, sharing, and laughing together is important for our health.

Today in our society, both children and adults eat fast food several times a week. They spend more and more time inside, away from nature, absorbed with television, video games, and the internet. No wonder we are miserable. We are isolated and alone in front of our technology without touch or eye contact. Pearl S. Buck, 1938 Nobel Prize Winner for Literature said, "The lack of emotional security of our American young people is due, I believe, to their isolation from the larger family unit. No two people—no mere father and mother—as I have often said, are enough to provide emotional security for a child. He needs to feel himself one in a world of kinfolk, persons of variety in age and temperament, and yet allied to himself by an indissoluble bond which he cannot break if he could, for nature has welded him into it before he was born."

For an example of how this isolation might affect health, we can look to a 2005 study in *Health Psychology* where Sheldon Cohen, Ph.D. and colleagues discovered that first-year college students with smaller social networks and greater reported loneliness had a poorer immune response to flu vaccine than other students. Learning how to build a community, a network, if you will, is important. Learning it is *normal* to expect happiness from materialism and practicing the poor habit of being isolated with our "things" can begin in childhood. Once these things are learned as a habitual lifestyle, it is very difficult to change.

Our society suffers from an epidemic of stress-related illness: obesity, heart disease, depression, anxiety-related disorders, cancers, and more. People avoid creating time for family, nature, and healthy practices because it contradicts the desire to attain more materialistic items and time-consuming activities. However, if you cannot make time for these critical components in your life, then you—and your family—will suffer the consequences.

We need to be healthier as a society because people are dying from stress-related illness!"

People are dying from poor nutrition!

People are dying because they are looking for a quick cure instead of a permanent cure!

People are dying because they refuse to go outside to walk and exercise!

People are dying from loneliness and isolation!

People are dying because of poor health and the fact they are no longer connected to nature!

My heart says that this is a tragedy, and it is time to stand up and take back our emotional and physical health.

People from all walks of life are flocking to their doctors for antidepressant prescriptions as a solution to their stressful and intimidating lives, yet very few report truly distressing levels of mental health problems. This tells me that we are driven as a society to get an answer like the one I was searching for earlier in my own life: the quick and easy "fix" of taking a pill versus the more time-consuming tactic of building a healthy lifestyle. With global pharmaceutical revenues at over 600 billion dollars, pharmaceutical companies love this approach. Instead of taking a pill, I say the answer might be to ask your doctor for a *prescription to a better lifestyle* so you can enhance the level of satisfaction in your life. That might include a counselor, a well-rounded diet, vitamins, and an exercise program to build energy levels instead of pills. The formula is quite simple: improve your lifestyle, have more energy, and be less miserable!

There is an answer!

There is a better solution to getting healthy with no drugs and no expensive diets. There is an answer which is revolutionary in its nature because it can be, for some people, a miracle cure for a stressful and unhealthy life.

The Go Green Health Plan is the beginning of making a difference for yourself and your family and was developed when I finally realized there is no quick and easy solution to having a whole healthy body. The hard reality: everything worth having is hard work. Another reality: perfection is unattainable. Learning to accept the human body as a total system and accepting yourself for who you are is clearly the most satisfying route you can take to achieve better health so you can feel good everyday.

By following the Go Green Health Plan, you can truly begin to change your life—your emotional AND physical life—for the better!

Go Green Health Plan*:

Step 1 Exercise aerobically, preferably outdoors in nature, for at least twenty minutes everyday, breathing deeply.

Step 2 Be exposed to daylight without sunglasses for twenty minutes everyday.

Step 3 Take multi-vitamins (with B vitamins included).

Step 4 Eat nutritionally between three and five meals/snacks everyday spaced apart as evenly as possible. Be sure these meals are small to moderate and have some form of a high-quality, low-fat protein and whole-grain carbohydrate.

Step 5 Get regular massage from a family member, a friend, or a professional.

Step 6 Regularly do helpful things for others and/or for the community and environment.

*NOTE: It is important to check with your doctor before participating in this or any health plan.

Chapter Four

Strip Away The Excuses—How To Make The Health Plan A Reality

∞

Y ou want to know how to feel better in your life—how to be less stressed, less depressed, and more satisfied? I believe the answer is in learning the connection between your brain and the environment. Seeing your life as a whole, versus treating individual parts of your body, will help you achieve overall well-being.

Take fad diets, for example. Why do so many try them? If you want to lose weight, you must go to the source of the weight gain. Understanding the reality that diets, dieting pills, and spot-solving exercise routines rarely work is important. Dieting is built on the premise that you can lose weight by following a restrictive diet which does not meet your total nutritional needs. Stop the diet, and you gain all the weight back because you move back into the same habits— the previous lifestyle that got you to gain the weight in the first place. Taking pills to solve your weight issues will not help your body remain healthy. There is not one pill you can take which will address the naked truth of your life. Taking pills is the dangerous way to try and find happiness. To solve health issues, you have to approach them from a scientific perspective. What does every good scientist do for their research? *Ask questions.*

Ask the right questions and you will get answers to move you in a positive direction. For example, "Why am I overweight?" The answer might be because you do not get regular exercise. "Why am I so stressed?" The answer might be because you are living an overwhelming lifestyle. "Why am I depressed and unhappy?" The answer might be because you are living in isolation. These are lifestyle choices. Of course, all of the answers are broken down to their simplest form. In reality, the answers can be extremely complex. Perhaps a person is overweight and stressed because of lifestyle patterns triggered by deep emotional scars. The problems are often complex and discovering the ultimate issue might involve discussions with your doctors. Solving them will require work and mutual cooperation.

Procrastination is another reason why some health improvement exercise programs never get off the ground. With a busy schedule, it is difficult to find time to go to the gym and work out in a prescribed format. It is difficult to stick to a rigid diet which can be dangerous and might not work anyway. So we procrastinate. I fell off my health plan when I overworked myself and felt I did not have the time to focus on my health. The reality is I did not have the time to forget about my health. One reason why I have been able to stick to my health plan now is I see every day how it makes me *feel* better. Let me repeat—*I feel better!* Not only that, after I practiced the health plan for a significant period of time, I realized I looked better, too. I feel better. I look better. I *am* better. This prevents me from procrastinating. It is a motivator. I am happy to walk everyday because it makes me feel so good. Many people tell me they want more energy. The lifestyle I am living gives me more energy. It can give you more energy too.

As far as all those necessary evils which you might be procrastinating, you know, the big ones like diet and exercise, the answer is simple. I know you will be frustrated when you hear this; but, in reality, diet and exercise does not have to be extreme. The answer is incredibly easy. Are you ready for this one? "All things in moderation!" Shocking cliché, eh? I look good and feel good because I exercise regularly, but I do not exercise heavily everyday. I refuse to eat an entire box of chocolate chip cookies, but I might have one. It allows me satisfaction without overindulgence and definitely follow the "all things in moderation" adage. I do, however, have dietary restrictions due to my allergies. Certain dietary restrictions are unique to individuals for other reasons as well, check with your doctor if you have special restrictions to see what foods might work best for you.

In reality, you do not have to sacrifice everything of who and what you are when you make positive changes to your lifestyle. For example, every morning I still have coffee. I enjoy it and it is one of my self-indulgences. However, the key is still "all things in moderation."

Certain things are easy in life—no-brainers—and one of those things is the strong desire to feel really good everyday. By improving your lifestyle like I have, you CAN. You do not want to procrastinate because you like feeling good about yourself and your lifestyle everyday.

To understand more about your personal requirements for a healthier lifestyle, be realistic. Ask the right questions, and understand there is no instant cure. Instead of asking symptom questions, ask better overall health questions, like "Why am I not healthy?" Understand the requirements your body and brain need to survive in this stress-filled world, and it will be easier for you to adopt a lifestyle change to meet those requirements. Take the time to understand; because, if you do not, you may never have more time to make these discoveries.

The Brain and Stress

To better understand why the six steps of the Go Green Health Plan are necessary, it is important to understand the effects of stress and how we process flow experiences within the human body.

It all starts with your brain. Your brain needs proper nutrition, regular exercise, sunlight, physical and emotional connection, and much, much more to function properly and cope with stress. Your brain is busy using neurotransmitters and other chemicals to send messages to all parts of your body twenty-four hours a day. It is a complex job. Add both the physical and emotional stress of modern times to this process; and your brain must work overtime to learn, grow, and maintain its health.

According to Dr. Richard O'Connor, in *Undoing Perpetual Stress*, the brain is a sub-system within our whole body system. It interacts with the immune, endocrine, and many other systems in the body to control our stress responses. From a scientific perspective, O'Connor says, "Scientists now have the tools and knowledge base to understand much more completely than ever before how the brain works. We can see how it is damaged by such things as child abuse and neglect, and emotional trauma in adult life. We are beginning to see how it is affected by chronic stress."

Richard O'Connor, Ph.D.

O'Connor goes on to describe how stressful events cause an immediate brain reaction, "...the brain immediately signals the release of hypothalamic, pituitary, and adrenal hormones. It signals the adrenal glands (just above the kidneys) to release cortisol and adrenaline, and the sympathetic nervous system to release norepinephrine all over the body. As a result, your heart beats faster, the hairs on the back of your neck stand up, you sweat, your stomach churns, and your bowels loosen." Many people in our very busy modern society are *constantly* stressed. This places your system in a constant stage of full-blown "fight-or-flight" response. This nonstop response scenario, in turn, allows the brain to send special chemicals to help us cope with the "emergency."

The chemical reaction our brain employs is quite amazing. According to O'Connor, "Your vision improves, your attention is focused, your memory improves, and you feel alert and powerful. This is a marvelous orchestration of the body to help us deal with danger. After the danger is passed, there is another complex regulatory system that returns things to normal. This process of maintaining equilibrium is referred to as allostasis. When we feel that the danger does not go away, the mechanisms underlying allostasis get damaged, and we lose the ability to return ourselves to normal."

Imagine most people in our society under this heavy stress. Our bodies will be producing very high levels of cortisol regularly. Too much cortisol makes us vulnerable to ulcers by thinning the lining of the stomach, changing bone structure, and damaging several systems within our body, including the reproductive and immune systems. This leads to increased susceptibility to colds and infections. The interference with growth hormones and insulin can lead to diabetic-centered disease. O'Connor continues, "It (cortisol) interferes with how we store fat, sending more of it to the abdomen, which is not only unsightly but is also a greater health threat than other kinds of fat. We turn to sugar and other comfort foods because they actually put a brake on the chronic stress response, but we put on weight and damage our health." If our society, on the large, is under constant stress, then, as a nation, our physical and emotional health is suffering.

Let's go back to that list of stress-related illnesses: obesity, heart disease, depression, and anxiety-related disorders. In my personal life, the connection was clear: stress was causing my body to react. Although not obese, the weight gain I do hold is in my abdomen. I have high blood pressure, and during stressful times I have difficulty coping. Stress also causes me to suffer a lack of sleep, mysterious and constant pain in my back, my allergy symptoms become extreme, the reaction triggers other illnesses—essentially my systems break down. This is what stress can do to you as well. Perhaps far worse symptoms plague you. Perhaps far less. Either way, stress is bad. Why keep the stress burden in your life? Although we must all cope with some level of stress, why not reduce it significantly so you might feel better—and look better—than you ever have? The Go Green Health Plan is based on significant ways to reduce and eliminate stress for your body.

Enjoyment of Activity and Life with Flow

A psychology professor, Mihaly Csikszentmihalyi, Ph.D. wrote *Flow: The Psychology of Optimal Experience*. His theories described in that book reflect his prime goal studies from 1963, which has been to learn more about the process of human enjoyment. In other words, what activity is fun and rewarding? That is a complex question. Some people enjoy art or hiking, some enjoy reading or biking, some enjoy working or carpentry, but what is the commonality between all of these "enjoyable" activities, and how can we apply this to better health?

Mihaly Csikszentmihalyi, Ph.D.

Csikszentmihalyi discovered a surprising answer which he describes as "flow". Flow is the pleasurable sensation of losing oneself in an activity—work, a game, a physical or mental challenge—and becoming immersed, with everything perfectly meshing in a harmonious state where goals are set and satisfyingly met. Flow, or "optimal experience," involves a contradictory balance between structure and release. It is an experience between concentrated focus on a goal and a feeling of mechanical effortlessness. Time contracts or stretches and the individual merges with the action, totally absorbed.

The following is an excerpt from Csikszentmihalyi's book *The Evolving Self*,

> "Contrary to expectation, 'flow' usually happens not during relaxing moments of leisure and entertainment, but rather when we are actively involved in a difficult enterprise, in a task that stretches our mental and physical abilities. Any activity can do it. Working on a challenging job, riding the crest of a tremendous wave, and teaching one's child the letters of the alphabet are the kinds of experiences that focus our whole being in a harmonious rush of energy, and lift us out of the anxieties and boredom that characterize so much of everyday life.

"It turns out that when challenges are high and personal skills are used to the utmost, we experience this rare state of consciousness. The first symptom of flow is a narrowing of attention on a clearly defined goal. We feel involved, concentrated, absorbed. We know what must be done, and we get immediate feedback as to how well we are doing. The tennis player knows after each shot whether the ball actually went where she wanted it to go; the pianist knows after each stroke of the keyboard whether the notes sound like they should. Even a usually boring job, once the challenges are brought into balance with the person's skills and the goals are clarified, can begin to be exciting and involving.

"The depth of concentration required by the fine balance of challenges and skills precludes worrying about temporarily irrelevant issues. We forget ourselves and become lost in the activity. If the rock-climber were to worry about his job or his love life as he is hanging by his fingertips over the void, he would soon fall. The musician would hit a wrong note, the chess player would lose the game.

"The well-matched use of skills provides a sense of control over our actions, yet because we are too busy to think of ourselves, it does not matter whether we are in control or not, whether we are winning or losing. Often we feel a sense of transcendence, as if the boundaries of the self had been expanded. The sailor feels at one with the wind, the boat, and the sea; the singer feels a mysterious sense of universal harmony. In those moments the awareness of time disappears, and hours seem to flash by without our noticing.

"This state of consciousness ... comes as close as anything can to what we call happiness.... "

Meditation can also cause a flow experience for participants. Learning about Csikszentmihalyi's flow theories helped me understand why my blood pressure goes down during garden season. My doctor advised me that the easiest way to lower blood pressure is to learn to meditate. I was unable to grasp the concept of meditation, although I had tried many times. Finally, however, being outside in the environment and fresh air, working with the plants, putting my toes in the dirt—these things put me into a very focused state, a state of flow. Being outdoors often has a similar effect on children and adults alike. Gardening, in particular, unites the human body with nature and the environment.

This is why some say, "weeding is therapy." Repetitive work develops a sense of flow as much as a more specifically creative activity. This also explains why some people work until retirement, then die the year they retire. Losing a flow activity means losing an activity which buoys the heart and the mind of a human being. Some feel lost, lonely, depressed, and the brain immediately reacts. Their health quickly deteriorates.

A surprising find for Csikszentmihalyi was related to television, "People seem to get more flow from what they do on their jobs than from leisure activities in free time." It turns out that watching TV is not at all a flowful activity. People generally report higher levels of stress, depression, and tension after watching TV. It seems that TV's main virtue is that it occupies the mind without effort. Flow is hard to achieve without effort. Flow is not "wasting time."

The Go Green Health Plan encourages flow activities and stimulates the positive brain chemicals and body activity our system needs to feel better mentally and physically. It is a whole mind-and-body health plan.

Step 1   Exercise aerobically, preferably outdoors in nature, for at least twenty minutes everyday, breathing deeply.

Moderate exercise is necessary for good health and is particularly effective in reducing stress symptoms and alleviating depression and anxiety.

Physical exercise in the garden provides exposure to the outdoor environment and enhances flow experiences which can bring me to a more meditative state. This includes repetitive activities like weeding, digging, and building. Many people achieve this state of flow while bicycling or performing other forms of exercise. I am not here to suggest which exercise is the perfect fit for your lifestyle or how hard you should exert yourself. This is a discussion between you and your health provider. Exceptionally strenuous work in the garden is not necessary to feel good. However, I am more likely to hit a meditative state if I practice the exercise for close to sixty minutes. During the non-gardening season, I walk everyday that I can for at least twenty to thirty minutes. Over time, I have increased that to longer periods and a brisker pace.

There are other reasons exercise is important for good health. The cortisol by-products of the fight-or-flight stress response continue to circulate in the body and have the potential to create physical illness even after the stress response has dissipated. Regular exercise is useful in removing by-products of the stress response by providing the opportunity to simulate the fighting or running dictated by the fight or flight phenomenon. As such, regular exercise allows the body to return to normal faster and reduce the physical impact of psycho-social stress.

Regular exercise can enhance a good night's rest. Many people find that regular exercise brings better sleep. For a stressed-out body, that alone can be a healing experience.

Recent research has documented the important role that expression or repression of anger and hostility plays in disease progression. Exercise is also a great outlet for anger and hostility. Used properly, exercise provides a socially acceptable means of physically releasing negative energy.

From an emotionally health perspective, high levels of self-esteem and self-efficacy have been correlated with increased ability to cope with high stress levels. Regular exercise cultivates self-esteem and enhances feelings of well-being.

Endorphins have been shown to increase during physical activity of twenty minutes or more. Chemically similar to opiate compounds, these morphine-like substances have been shown to provide a pain-relieving effect and promote a sense of euphoria. Some experts describe this as a "runner's high." In general, the positive moods linked with regular exercise are significant.

A demonstration of how exercise in nature can have an immediate effect on stress is to follow this quick tip. If a social stressor like an argument or multi-tasking experience becomes too overwhelming, why not remove yourself from the situation? Take five minutes away from the stressful event, preferably outside in nature. Concentrate on breathing deeply and doing a physical exercise of some sort, like stretching or knee bends. I believe you get an even better benefit if you exercise for fifteen minutes. Take the same breather, get away from the event, and walk around the block for fifteen minutes. When you return to the situation, you will be calmer and have a clearer focus.

It is true that simply taking a break from a stressful moment, be it outdoors or inside, is a good thing to do. However, I feel it is specifically important to take a break, if you are able, by exercising in nature. I believe this is true because of research conducted by the University of Illinois Landscape and Human Health Laboratory team has been doing on the subject of human interaction with the natural environment. Most significant is the 2001 study on how Chicago public housing residents who lived in apartment buildings which were surrounded by trees and greenery had forty-eight percent fewer property crimes and fifty-six percent fewer violent crimes than identical apartment buildings barren of greenery. It is quite remarkable to note that even modest amounts of greenery were linked with lower crime rates.

The researchers suggested one of the reasons crime was reduced might be that exposure to greenery reduces aggression by helping people to relax and de-stress. They based this claim on prior research showing an association between viewing nature and less mental fatigue. Another reason suggested for their finding was that crime was reduced partly because the green space around those buildings have en-couraged more people in the community to come outdoors, thereby discouraging criminals by increasing community supervision. They also suggested that buildings and communities that have a landscaped appearance might be more likely to show potential criminals that residents care about and watch over their property. Based on this research, taking a calming exercise break by gardening or walking outdoors in a green environment seems a more positive way to relieve stress.

Walking is convenient to almost everyone. You do not have to buy into an

Shawna getting some physical exercise in the early Spring garden. Photo by Kelsey Connors.

expensive health club to exercise for twenty or thirty minutes everyday you can step right outside your front door for a nice walk and achieve excellent results. Exercising out in nature gives you energy and lifts your spirits.

Many scientists suggest that music can also help lift your spirit and help encourage you through daily exercise. I agree, particularly if you need stronger motivation to get yourself outside. In this modern world filled with MP3 and portable music players, it seems a great idea to combine your outdoor exercise activity with music. However, my opinion on music is it should be energetic to improve mood. If you are listening to a very slow and tedious piece of music, it might be relaxing, but is not conducive to lifting one's emotions and physical energy to improve mood. Yes, it is necessary in a very stressed-out world to relax once in a while, but remember all I have discussed about flow and brain chemicals? Motivating yourself with *energizing* music will help to lift your heel, so you walk a little faster on your route, or dig a little deeper in the garden. Being energized is the best part about the Go Green Health Plan—it is what makes you feel so good.

My recommendation is to exercise aerobically, preferably outdoors in nature, for at least twenty minutes everyday, breathing deeply. Keep in mind the theory of "all things in moderation," simply getting out and doing something is better than sitting on your derrière in front of the television. So go do it!!

Step 2 Be exposed to daylight without sunglasses for twenty minutes everyday.

How come when you walk outside on a sunny spring day you feel *fantastic*? You know the feeling– the incredible rush of energy that leaves you whistling a tune and happily bouncing along. That is when I clear my schedule. Spending the entire day outdoors in the garden is wonderful therapy for me—both physically and emotionally.

It was just that type of day, a few years ago, which inspired me to contact several doctors and ask them how I can harness that rush of energy. Gardening or walking in nature on days like that are inspiring. I accomplish far more, feel far better, and enjoy the work. It is easy to hit a state of flow more quickly, and I feel like I could conquer the world.

One theory regarding that feeling is that, when the naked eye directly perceives daylight, our brain receives a chemical message of increased serotonin levels. We feel a rush of positive energy due to increased serotonin levels. Popular medical opinion says serotonin is even more significant than flow. Serotonin is a chemical found in your brain that is believed to play an important role as a

Shawna and her favorite assistant, Harry the pug, out in the sunlight. Photo by Kelsey Connors.

neurotransmitter. It helps regulate emotions and mood, aggression, body temperature, sleep, vomiting, sexuality, and appetite, among other things. More important, it helps you feel like a million bucks on a beautiful spring day.

Dr. David Edelberg, M.D., confirms this in his book, *The Triple Whammy Cure*. The book, although applicable to most everyone, focuses on women's health. I found Dr. Edelberg's ideas particularly inspiring in relationship to improving serotonin levels. Dr. Edelberg states that serotonin is a neurotransmitter in your brain which provides strong resistance against stress. The more serotonin you have, the better you are able to tolerate all types of stress. He also says that women have less serotonin than men do, which makes them more susceptible to stress in general.

Sunlight exposure is the number one drug-free way our bodies create additional serotonin according to Dr. Edelberg. He also suggests that exercise, diet, and laughter can stimulate increased levels of serotonin. Let me remind you—laughter is *free*.

There are certain eye conditions, such as macular degeneration, that worsen with exposure to sunlight. If you suspect you have this condition or something similar,

Dr. David Edelberg, M.D.

please contact your doctor for his advice before following this portion of the Go Green Health Plan. Also, follow as many of the other steps in the Go Green Health Plan as you can and find other ways to increase serotonin, like exercise, positive thinking, and laughter.

Also, it is very important to wear sunscreen while working outdoors. This is critical even on cloudy days as the sun's rays are powerful and can easily overwhelm precious skin when least expected.

Remember, expose yourself to daylight for twenty minutes everyday and your mood and ability to handle stress should significantly improve.

Step 3   Take multi-vitamins (with B vitamins included).

Vitamins. The eternal debate between homeopaths and medical doctors can loom before you and frighten you from taking any vitamin pills at all.

I was not a pro-vitamin person until I fell off my health plan, got extremely stressed-out, became run down, and was diagnosed with anemia. Never have I missed a day since. We cannot completely eliminate stress from our modern day life. Living a stressful lifestyle without vitamins, in my opinion, is a prescription for disaster. All of my doctors, both specialists and family practitioners, recommend at least the basic multi-vitamin as a supplement to a well-balanced diet. Experts such as Dr. Andrew Weil and Dr. David Edelberg concur. In this day and age of fast food and no-time-for-cooking, it is one of the first things we should consider to maintain good health.

My daily vitamin and supplement regimen includes a multi-vitamin, a B formula vitamin, acidophilus and St. John's Wort. Your particular combination might be different. My doctors tell me it is important to consume the vitamins on a full stomach, preferably following a meal for quick absorption.

Andrew Weil, M.D., author of *Natural Health, Natural Medicine*, says he is not a great fan of taking pills, and believes we should get the bulk of our nutritional needs from our diets. His concern is that the average person might not be eating a well-rounded diet. He does see the need for taking additional vitamins, especially by people who face a large amount of stress. I take vitamins because

Andrew Weil, M.D.

I face daily stresses that would make a world leader crumble to the ground and cry like a baby. Running several businesses, plus playing taxi to a busy family, not to mention cooking, banking, cleaning, organizing, mailing, and volunteering. This, for most modern day Americans, is a normal life. It is nonstop and totally overwhelming! Our bodies and our brains are stressed. We need exercise, a good night's rest, a proper diet and, YES—vitamins.

My doctors know what vitamins I take and have approved. I suggest you ask your doctor for further recommendations on supplements and vitamins. Get started taking them today!

Step 4   Eat nutritionally between three to five meals/snacks everyday, spaced apart as evenly as possible. Be sure these meals are small to moderate and have some form of high-quality, low- protein and whole-grain carbohydrates.

One of the most important components to the Go Green Health Plan is eating nutritionally. Additionally, you should drink water often. This plan will keep your stress levels at a manageable level and you will feel healthier, stronger, and better able to handle what is tossed at you on a daily basis.

It makes sense to think that, if your body and brain need chemicals in liquid form to travel from point to point, you need to regularly supply your body with water. According to F. Batmanghelidj, M.D., author of *Water for Health, for Healing, for Life*, blood, when it is properly hydrated, is about ninety-four percent water. Having the correct volume of blood will ensure that nutrients move through and are processed by your body adequately. Drinking water will encourage your body to produce the correct volume of hydrated blood cells. I have learned to choose water more often than not, but still enjoy my morning coffee and indulge in a soda once in a while. Again, indulge in moderation!

When you experience stress, all parts of your mind and body are affected. Your entire body experiences changes that will worsen if not dealt with. When you ignore your diet, particularly when you are stressed, your immune system can become compromised, leading to more frequent illness. Your moods can fluctuate severely. This is definitely true for me. Eating several small, protein-based meals throughout the day keep my emotions more even. Remaining calm, particularly when under stress, is possible if I have five smaller meals per day versus two or three very large ones.

Mark Twain once quipped that the only way to stay healthy is to "eat what you don't want, drink what you don't like and do what you'd druther not." Nothing could be farther from the truth! Eating nutritionally means more flavor and more variety, not sacrifice. I still have a cocktail once in a while, and I still enjoy rich or fried foods. However, by practicing the "all things in moderation" motto when preparing and eating foods, I am better for it.

Plant-based foods fill you up with nutrients and typically have less fat and cholesterol. Fruits, vegetables, and whole grains are the best places to start a great diet, mostly because they are high in fiber, high in vitamins, and low in fat. Fill your plate full. I am not a vegetarian, although I see the benefits of eating mostly vegetables and have come to enjoy vegetables as much as anything else on my plate.

Eating fresh, locally grown foods is both nutritious and energy-conscious. Organic foods are p*roduced without chemically formulated fertilizers, growth stimulants, antibiotics, or pesticides.* Buying foods that are organic is a preferred choice in my opinion. Why feed yourself and your family unwanted chemicals and antibiotics? We do not know their long-term dilatory effects yet. It makes sense to err on the side of caution.

There is an additional consideration. Can you find out where the organic foods originated? Sometimes organic foods are imported from distant countries. Think about the extensive transportation materials and fuels which are wasted when bringing foreign organic foods to your table. Growing up on a farm, I understand what is involved in the labor and production of the average farm product. The farmer might or might not use equipment to plow, plant, and harvest his yield. If he does, significant carbon-producing equipment is used to produce his organic foods. For the average crop, a tractor with a plow attachment drives up and down the length of the fields, plowing the earth under. Then a second trip over the field cultivates the dirt into a more seed-receptive consistency. A third trip over the field will be needed for planting seeds. Then the plants begin to grow. This is the time most non-organic farmers go over the field a fourth time and possibly a fifth time to treat with weed-killing chemicals. When it is time to harvest, farmers either pick their product by hand or drive a special harvesting vehicle over the field, such as a combine, to harvest the organic product.

At this point, a farmer might be able to drive his produce directly to a local grocery store. He might use further equipment and utilities to pack the product in special containers to ensure its freshness. An organic farmer who farms overseas has to get his produce to a distributor, or hire someone to drive it to the distributor. An international distributor holds the product, has regulation officials drive over to inspect the product, repacks the product (usually using energy-consuming packing equipment and material), and drives it to customs with specific shipping orders. Then he has the produce packed in trains, planes, or trucks to be shipped to its next destination.

If the produce comes via plane to the United States, then the product is stored in a customs waiting facility. Customs agents inspect the product and keep it at the warehouse for a required period of time (sometimes weeks for coffee beans and other similar products). Once it passes inspection, a distributor comes to pick up the product via truck and delivers the product to its own wholesale warehouses where it sometimes sits and awaits repacking before being distributed via more trucks out to specific retail stores. Then it sits in special air-conditioned units to keep the product cool until the consumer buys it. The air-conditioned units most of us see at the grocery stores, which keep apples and other produce cool, typically have no "lid." They are open air machines which must remain constantly "on" and pumping to maintain the produce at a certain temperature. Then the grocers hope and pray that someone buys the product. If no one does, the produce is thrown out and all of that energy will have been wasted for no reason. *This* explains why produce costs so much. Grocers must pay for the enormous transportation fees and energy costs it takes to maintain the product.

This long process also explains why a lot of produce from the grocery store has no taste. Remember the farmer? Certain types of produce have to be picked by the farmer when they are still unripe so they can survive the entire long distance shipping process to the end consumer. A tomato, picked when it is not fully ripe and fresh off the vine, will taste bland when it finally does ripen—unnaturally—by sitting on a shelf. That is why the best tasting tomatoes are at your grocery store mid-summer—it is the season for them. This is also why local organic farmers have an advantage. By cutting out all those middle people who are in shipping and distribution, they bring a fresher, riper, and tastier product filled with far more vitamins to your grocer's door.

Do you see the outrageous amount of vehicles, gasoline and energy that it takes to send all types of produce material from other countries to the United States and Canada? Buying local means more produce filled with vitamins and flavor for your family and more energy savings for the world. It makes better sense. *Buy local!*

Think about it. What is doing you and your family the most harm? The chemicals in your food by purchasing nonorganic produce? Or perhaps the chemicals in the air and water released from vehicles during the transportation process? It is a difficult question to answer as we do not have produce regulation at the level where we can calculate everything involved in transport. Not only that, think how long ago the foods were picked or processed. Is it better to buy a product that has been in transportation for months, even if it is organic? Or is it better to buy a locally grown product, recently picked, which has more vitamins and nutritionally positive components because it has not had time to break down yet?

I say locally grown products are the best, both for our bodies and our environment. Try and keep this in mind when you are grocery shopping. Providing the best chemically-free and pollution-free nutrition is important for all human being's health.

Meat can be organic as well. Ask questions and find out where it really comes from and all the details. Most of my meals include regular low-fat proteins in meat and nut form. A regular, varied diet which includes low-fat protein, whole-grain carbohydrates, and vegetables is best for me. Do I sometimes splurge? Of course! My favorite food is filet mignon. I love it! I rarely eat desserts, but enjoy a cocktail after dinner. Caffeinated coffee and tea have always been a part of my diet, but remember my mantra, "all things in moderation." I follow this rule faithfully and try not to overdo. By following this way of thinking, both in consideration of where your food comes from and the types of foods you eat, you will ingest less chemicals and add more variety to your diet.

As I mentioned before, I have discovered it is very important to eat at regular intervals throughout the day. Eating a small meal five times a day seems to improve my mood and help me cope better than eating two or three large meals. Experts concur. Face it, you've heard this lecture over and over on television, in the news and on the cover of many health magazines—you must eat regularly and eat healthy to keep your system working the way it should.

Step 5   Get regular massage from a family member, a friend, or a professional.

Regular human touch and, specifically, massage is important. Dr. Andrew Weil in *Natural Health, Natural Medicine*, says that massage can be especially relaxing and healing. He says that one must get massage regularly to receive the full benefits. I agree. It is like exercise. Exercising just once is good, but will not help your body over the long term. You must exercise regularly to get the benefits. The same is true of massage and touch. I feel it can be one of the singularly most healing experiences in a person's life.

There is more to massage than the therapy of manipulating muscles. I believe in the power of touch and so do hundreds of medical doctors who testify to the benefits of touch, hugs, and massage. Dr. David Edelberg reminds us in *The Triple Whammy Cure*, that caring touch can relax stressed muscles and amplify feelings of well-being by increasing feel-good endorphins like serotonin.

According to the Associated Bodywork & Massage Professionals, "research continues to show the enormous benefits of touch—which range from treating chronic diseases, neurological disorders, and injuries, to alleviating the tensions of modern lifestyles. Consequently, the medical community is actively embracing bodywork, and massage is becoming an integral part of hospice care and neonatal intensive care units. Many hospitals are also incorporating on-site massage practitioners and even spas to treat post-surgery or pain patients as part of the recovery process."

The reason I encourage massage is because I have felt the benefits. When my husband and I were first married he often massaged my feet. It always felt good; but after a while I noticed, whenever he rubbed my feet, I could breathe easier. The connection did not make sense to me—I mean the one between my feet and lungs—but whatever the connection, it helped relieve serious allergy symptoms whenever he placed strong pressure along the center of my foot. Delicate massage was not the key for me. Firm pressure had to be applied for the effects to be fully felt. At the time it was a joy, but when I became pregnant and could no longer use certain over-the-counter medications to relieve my allergy symptoms, it became a necessity. His daily foot massages were simply "heaven on earth," and it brought us closer together emotionally as well as physically. Later, I felt a similar effect when he massaged my sinuses or lower back.

If the condition became more than my husband and I could handle I would go to a professional. My favorite massage therapist is Kimberly Stillwell, a Certified Massage Therapist who ons Navitus massage Therapy. Her experienced back massages regularly helped prevent a visit to the emergency room. If my back would "go out" to the point I could not walk, I found a visit to a medical doctor necessary to confirm there was not damage to the spine or lumbar region. Then rest, gentle stretching, and massage would be the only things to relieve both the pain and the muscle spasms. Stillwell feels that, "There is a heightened sense of well being when receiving a massage, not only from the human contact and energy exchange that takes place between client and therapist, but also from the manual manipulation and points pressed that release tension and increase circulation and blood flow. "

Stillwell chose massage therapy as a career because she feels it is an inspirational and beautiful way to contribute to the human race. As she says, "Massage allows the recipient to open him or herself to a greater sense of self from a physical, emotional, and a spiritual standpoint as well." Massage is a tremendous gift to give to another human being. Her belief is that the power of human touch can make a difference in people's lives, particularly in the lives of so many who live so isolated from each other in today's society.

Kimberly Stillwell, CMT, promotes wellness and massage at Navitus Massage.

Remember, you do not have to pay a massage therapist to receive massage. Modern day etiquette says it is not always appropriate to ask a friend to massage your shoulder, but it is perfectly acceptable to have a massage therapist do it because it becomes a "medical treatment." As much as I love my excellent massage therapist, this makes no sense to me. Who better to help you with a sore muscle than a friend or family member? The massager feels wonderful helping you. Quite frankly, you feel wonderful knowing the massager is working out what might be a painfully sore muscle. You become closer to another human being. We need to be closer to one another. It seems like a win-win situation we should all try once in a while. If you do feel uncomfortable asking a friend, check with your health insurance and see if your insurance company will assist you financially by including massage therapy as part of your coverage.

There is a new trend developing for massage clubs where individuals go to a public gym wearing their gym clothes, much like an aerobics class. The massagers are lead through massage techniques by a professional masseuse. It is a great way to get the regular benefits of massage in a comfortable and relaxed atmosphere for a lesser cost. If there is not a massage club in your area, why not start one?

Another alternative is a non-licensed student. During my pregnancy, I was massaged by a masseuse-in-training for no charge at all. All massage therapists must earn a number of massage hours before they can become licensed. Perhaps having a masseuse-in-training would give you a no or low-cost alternative to a fully licensed massage therapist.

Self massage relieves pain and has noticeable benefits also. My doctors taught me massage techniques, combined with heat therapy, which I use to relieve sinus headaches. This has been a great source of pain relief during some of my heightened allergy attacks. However, self massage cannot address the simple, yet healing act, of one person touching another person.

As human beings, we all need touch. Mothers hug their children. Husbands hug their wives. Children hug each other and their pets. It is proven that we all need this touch. By giving massage, or even a hug, we help relieve our own stress as well as stress in other people's lives. It is the first step to reaching out to others and living a physical and emotionally healthy experience.

Step 6   Regularly do helpful things for others, for the community and the environment.

There are a host of reasons for doing helpful things for others and your community. Right at the top is the stress reduction you get from building personal relationships and expanding your community network. Dr. Edelberg, in *The Triple Whammy Cure*, says people who volunteer to help others regularly have much higher levels of serotonin. Helping others actually increases your feel-good brain chemicals; and, therefore, helps *you*. Random acts of kindness can be most rewarding—your brain feeds you a gift in return for the kindness. The phrase, "you get as good as you give," takes on a whole new meaning when you consider Dr. Edelberg's view.

Many experts agree with Dr. Edelberg and take it further by suggesting we should all reinforce community and friendships. According to the authors of *YOU: The Owners Manual*, Michael Roizen, M.D. and Mehmet C. Oz, M.D., the most reliable stress reducers to help both depression and anger are consistent exercise, regular meditation, and cultivation of friendships.

C. Everett Koop, M.D. has a Time Life Medical book called *Dr. Koop's Self-Care Advisor*. In this book he describes a study which revealed that single people who felt they did not have a confidante with whom to discuss their intimate thoughts were three times more likely to die within a five-year period than those who had someone close to talk to.

It seems that social isolationism and a lack of concern for both family and neighborhood communities can be hazardous to your health by increasing stress levels and preventing brain building activity which social activities encourage.

Being active in your family community may mean getting closer to both your immediate and more distant family. Coming together with people you love is important. Being active and building neighborhood community can do a lot as well. You can work on projects, which I encourage, like neighborhood-focused environmental efforts.

There are many lonely neighbors who live by themselves or who are older and could use your caring help. Bringing these people together can be particularly rewarding for the community. Perhaps you can build a garden, help shut-ins or get your city to create walking paths for its residents. The important idea is to come together with others and build relationships. You will be caring for yourself, your neighbors and the Earth. You will be empowering others to feel better and be better.

In my mind, it is also important to give completely of your heart. This is part of what it means to come together as a community. Giving your money, your time, your generosity to others can make a drastic improvement in your life and the lives of the people you are helping. Even if you have no money, you will always have your heart. Sharing your heart and kindness with others can improve your health by stimulating those feel good chemicals in your brain.

Several years ago, my neighborhood joined together to provide a "Yard Sale Benefit" for a family who lived on our street and needed financial support. The project was a great feel-good effort which brought together our small community. It was also environmentally friendly as it helped keep clothing, furniture, and other "junk" out of the landfills. Each family on the block contributed by placing yard sale items in their front yard so that shoppers could walk around the entire

It was a rewarding experience for our community to come together and help our neighbors with a fund raising yard sale. Baked goods were sold by the Vinsel family and profits all went to our neighbor who needed financial support.

circle and purchase. We sold baked goods and drinks as well. The event was quite a success and we all grew closer because of it. Get to know your neighbors. Maybe there is an isolated soul who could really use your friendship and help living right next door to you.

Neighbors Kathy Chamberlain, Nancy Dunham, and friends unite to offer each other support during the fund raising event.

Giving and sharing with others for a healthier environment, a healthier you, a healthier world makes you feel better and makes the world a better place to live. There is no question in my mind that doing things for my personal community—my family and my neighborhood—have taught me to be a better person and made me healthier along the way.

With my heart and my soul, I believe that one person can make a difference. One person CAN teach and inspire the people of the world to grow together in a healthy way. It is worth every effort you put forth to understand that the steps you are taking to give and care for others will be reflected back on you ten fold. Call it good karma, call it good will, I like to call it simply—GOOD!

Life is often tragic and difficult. So many people feel unhealthy, depressed, and overwhelmed by hopelessness in today's stress-filled society. By helping the greater community, you pull yourself out of this stressful quagmire and bring all

Families all came together to support the effort. Here Dan and Robert LaDeur load furniture onto a vehicle at the community yard sale benefit.

the people you touch along for the ride. I believe that each one of us can do our part in saving the world. Making a difference and caring for people is more than something you should do—it is something we all *must* do for our on-going survival in this universe.

Chapter Five

Naked Action—Examples From Real Life

∞

Get busy and spark yourself into action to get healthy! Sometimes the most difficult step in this journey is the very first step. I am there with you. Taking that first step was hard for me; but now that I have done it, I better manage my health and my outlook on life. This chapter will encourage you by demonstrating how others have made positive changes in their lives, too.

All It Takes Is Fifteen Claps

That's right; it takes the average person only fifteen steps to get off the couch and to the front door. Right now, set this book down and clap fifteen times. That is equivalent to fifteen steps to get you out the front door.

Imagine what you can accomplish in fifteen claps; you can get off your fanny and open the front door. You can introduce yourself to someone in your community. You can take your recycling containers from the garage to the end of your driveway. Each one sounds like a small accomplishment. Yet, each is a significant accomplishment when you consider that the first steps are often the most difficult. You can do it right now. It's easy: clap fifteen times and step out the door for a break in nature.

The benefits from exercising in nature are numerous. On top of all the benefits of getting healthier and greener, building a simple garden in your neighborhood can improve your concentration and self-discipline. Also, it can decrease aggression and violence in your community. With your family and neighborhood communities exposed regularly to positive environmental practices and green vegetation, you can make a difference in reducing crime rates surrounding your home.

This sounds like an outlandish claim, yet proof is found in groundbreaking research done by the University of Illinois Landscape and Human Health Laboratory. Their research states, "Children growing up in the inner city are at risk of academic underachievement, juvenile delinquency, teenage pregnancy, and other important negative outcomes. Avoiding these outcomes requires self-discipline. Self-discipline, in turn, may draw on directed attention, a limited resource that can be renewed through contact with nature."

The amazing results of that research and testing, particularly in relationship to girls, reveal that, on average, the greener a girl's view from her home, the better she concentrates, the better she is at inhibiting impulses, and the better she is able to delay gratification. This means that exposure to nature is more likely to generate a self-disciplined mindset, which is an important personal characteristic when trying to survive in a stressful world. If a girl has strong self-discipline, she is more likely to do well in school and in life, while avoiding unhealthy or risky behaviors.

Landscaped and vegetative views have been proven to reduce violence and improve mental state. Having a view of nature, as well as participating in nature, has been proven to make a difference.

The same team from the University of Illinois conducted an additional study on aggression. This study discovered that contact with vegetation reduces mental fatigue. The research was done in a setting and population with comparatively high rates of aggression: inner-city urban public housing residents. The study shows that, after studying 145 adult women, "levels of aggression and violence were significantly lower among individuals who had some nearby nature outside their apartments than among their counterparts who lived in barren conditions."

In other words, it is possible to be more emotionally healthy with regular exposure to nature. Being active while outdoors specifically increasing your physical movement can also improve your health. Remaining isolated and indoors prevents healthy exposure to the natural environment.

Getting healthier also means eating better foods—vegetables fresh from your garden and from local produce farmers. Having an improved mood and better attitude starts with the types of foods you feed your brain. Being outdoors more, eating better and living better can change a person's life.

This chapter cites several examples of people who choose to live every day by cultivating a healthy lifestyle. These people know the connection of health, greening, and nature and are working toward enhancing that connection to live a better life.

In the end, we humans must find a healthy way to move forward. Standing in one place where you shout out stress and pain and suffering won't help much. To be healthy, make it happen like these people have. Stop complaining about the problems, get yourself off that couch, take the fifteen steps to the door and move outside in nature to feel better.

Feeling and Looking Great—Stu changed his Lifestyle!

Dykstra and Comet before his passionate lifestyle change.

It was a cold, rainy, January day when I met with Stuart Dykstra and his dog, Comet. Yet, the gray weather did not hold doom and gloom for Stuart. His good-natured spirit and healthy triumph over poor health is an inspiration.

Dykstra spent twenty years struggling with poor health. His work was stressful, he had poor eating habits, he was out of shape, and he wanted to feel better. As the director of natural resources for a construction company which specializes in environmentally-centered development, Dykstra had trouble keeping up with the extensive travel and field work required by his firm. When Dykstra was asked to go to Haiti to help find water for the citizens of the developing country, it resonated as good timing to achieve better health. Climbing mountains and tramping through jungles in Haiti would be exhausting. To jump start his professional goals of building a healthier world, he needed better physical health; he needed to start with himself.

In the end, the final inspiration for him to lose weight came in the form of an angel. Dykstra's mother was on her death bed and in her last worldly act, showed him that mortality is the legacy of every human. No matter what our life struggles are, we all live and we all die. His fast paced work life suddenly took on a different hue. His love for his family, and the message his special angel communicated abruptly made sense.

Dykstra said, "When my Mom was dying, she only had family left; and, in the end, that is all that was important to her. An illness can devastate the husk of our bodies; but with a family's love, you still have the most meaningful part of your life. Her health and her community meant everything. A billion dollars would not have made a difference to her when she was dying. What becomes important to every human being is your lifestyle. How you live every single day."

These comments made Dykstra think. He began to notice the poor health habits of others in his family. It became clear to him that, although he is still young, he might already be more than halfway through his life span. "The bottom line is really this: my mother's death helped shift my mentality from wanting more "things" and more money to striving for modesty and less materialism—placing more importance on living life the way it *should* be; the right way."

Animals often inspire people to exercise, and Comet, Dykstra's irrepressible golden retriever, was no exception. Comet enthusiastically agreed to walk three times a day to help Dykstra get into shape. When I walked with Dykstra and Comet on a wet January day, I felt my own mood lighten and my heart fill with

Dykstra working to find water for the people of Haiti.

smiles at Comet's crazy stick-chasing antics. Comet, brimming with energy, made tongue-lolling mad dashes up and down the length of the park, always turning to be sure his master was paying attention to him and always circling back to place his head lovingly in Dykstra's hand. What a dog! The daily walks became therapy for both Dykstra and Comet, and improved health for both of them.

This daily exercise in nature, combined with better food choices, soon shot Dykstra's weight down nearly sixty pounds. He jokingly began calling his weight loss plan "The Lazy Man's Diet," because it was so easy to do. It follows the principles of my Go Green Health Plan, a fantastic way to find more energy and feel fantastic everyday.

Dykstra's food choices became simpler. He swears it is so easy that anyone can do it: eat less meat, eat less fat and processed sugars, eat more vegetables, then ask this question before eating every meal, "Is this 'good earth' food?"

Dykstra defines "good earth" foods as those that go through the least amount of processing. These foods are fresh and have traveled the quickest route to the table. For example, an apple is less processed, has more fiber, and is fresher than a jar of apple sauce to which high fructose corn-syrup and other chemicals have been added. Fresh baked whole grain bread is processed less than white bread with chemicals added to extend shelf life.

With an "all things in moderation" attitude, Dykstra says he does not eliminate processed foods entirely, but he eats smaller portions of the foods which are more processed, and tries to eat larger portions of fresh vegetables and fruits. He eats several small meals instead of one or two large meals. Reading labels helps increase his understanding of what products are higher in fiber and lower in fat and sugar. He discovered was that foods which are fresher taste better and have a better consistency when eaten. Eating has become a positive experience, and Dykstra looks forward to meals. Eliminating food is not the key to this positive weight-loss

Stuart Dykstra on the coast of Haiti after weight loss and health regimen change—enjoying the healthier life.

experience; Dykstra eats plenty of foods at every meal. It is the type of foods he is focused on—the fresher, the better!

"We feel like we are immortal when we are young," says Dykstra, "but twenty years of poor health practices showed me this is unrealistic. When I lost the first twelve pounds—*only twelve pounds*—I felt it was incredibly life changing. It proved to me that I had been living an unhealthy life. Getting healthier is not about losing the weight, however, it is about changing your mindset and living a routine which is focused more exclusively on the important things in life.

I became more emotionally self-confident as well as physically confident when I started to see the pounds melt away. The daily walks outdoors improved my mood significantly and gave me more energy. I always thought I felt tired and ill because I was just 'getting old,' and I now know how wrong that attitude was. I was overweight and out of shape—that's why I felt the way I did. Stress and poor lifestyle choices were dragging me down and making me feel worn out all of the time. Now, sixty pounds lighter and a hundred times healthier, I feel energized and fantastic. It's amazing!"

Now Dykstra is setting new goals for his mental and physical health. One goal is to continue to help the people of Haiti find a way out of drought so humankind can have better living conditions. Another goal is to walk across the Midwest with Comet. His physical health and muscle tone has improved so much he knows he can do it. Dykstra is an inspiration to all because his positive health practices have put him in a position to help the global community as well as conquer any challenge that comes his way.

Stu's Good Earth Lazy Man's Food and Training Regimen

Dykstra's diet and training regimen, which helped him lose more than sixty pounds, is amazingly simple. His number one belief is that all things should be done or consumed in moderation. Read labels to understand food content. Remember, the fresher the food, the better it is for you.

Comet and his owner, Stuart Dykstra, walk all seasons—all weather—for the best possible physical health.

Food

- Eat less meat.
- Eat less fat and sugar.
- Eat more fiber and vegetables.
- Ask this question before eating every meal, "Is this good earth food?" If the answer is no, then consume less of it or do not consume it at all.

Exercise

- Walk your dog (or yourself) outside in nature for at least thirty minutes three times a day—once in the morning, once at lunch, and once in the evening. (Many people find it impossible to walk at noon. When you simply cannot work it in, stretch your morning and evening walks or do longer walks on the weekends.)

Do all of the above daily and enjoy!

Susan and Larry's Vegetable Garden—A Healing Retreat!

One of the most inspiring "naked action's" I learned about was done by a lovely couple, Susan and Larry Kasprowicz. Their actions touched me profoundly in their desire to improve both their physical and nutrition-based health. Both Susan and Larry understand that being healthier involves more than belonging to a health club. It involves participation in the community and in the greater world. Planting a fruit and vegetable garden is a healthy way to relieve stress and eat well. It is also healthy for the environment. It is much better to grow or buy 'local' produce rather than waste all the resources it takes to ship our food from faraway places.

Susan and Larry have been married for 25 years. They live in an older home in a small suburban community near Chicago, Illinois. Their backyard vegetable garden suffered when expansive maple trees totally covered the area with shade. Both Susan and Larry, avid vegetable gardeners, were perplexed when their garden produced smaller and smaller vegetables, and sometimes no vegetables. Shade was the problem. Not willing to cut down the maple trees, Susan decided to relocate their vegetable garden to the front yard.

Yes, I know, the front yard is traditionally a place for more formal gardening. Susan and Larry's garden is far from boring! Even though It is filled with vegetables, the garden is beautiful, creative, well organized, and decorative. This is a fun and relaxing spot to experience a nice afternoon. They took a risk and created an inspiring and beautiful space for all to share because of Larry's health issues.

Larry is a remarkable survivor. He has Type II diabetes and has survived colon cancer, so eating nutritionally is very important for him. However, that is not all that ails Larry. He has interstitial lung disease, sometimes called fibrocystic lung disease, complicated by emphysema, as well as congestive heart failure (CHF) and atrial fibrillation. Atria fibrillation means Larry was born with a hole in his heart. By the time he was diagnosed, he was in his 60s. Attempts to repair it

Susan and Larry Kasprowicz's front yard vegetable garden.

Susan and Larry posing in front of their health inspired garden.

were not successful. CHF is a byproduct of that experience because his lungs and heart have trouble working together.

Obviously, Larry's health is not what it used to be and he needs the physical and emotional therapy of planting a garden. Susan and Larry know that having daily exposure to nature makes a big difference for Larry, and therefore he is able to make a difference for the world. He is able to keep active and busy so he can keep his heart and lungs functioning well. Working in the garden also gives him the healthful benefits of outdoor activity, like increased levels of energy from serotonin exposure and regular exercise.

Visiting with Susan and Larry in their garden was so inspirational. Susan dotes on Larry, who has to carry a small oxygen container with him wherever he goes. Together they laugh, they create beautiful masterpieces, and they work to keep Larry's health in a better place. Together, in their garden, they are whole as they dig in the dirt and are in touch with the Earth. This is a place to share and be meditative, to enjoy the friendship and love they have for each other. And it is healthy—they are gardening nude.

During the off-season, Larry continues to stay active. He starts seeds for his garden in the heated garage under special grow-lights. Susan helps, but is guided by Larry's advice and direction. Susan says, "About 75 percent of what we grow starts out in the garage. In spring, the plants are moved in and out with the weather to harden them off. That keeps Larry busy from March through early May, and he's always proud of the results. Occasionally, we set out early tomatoes on St. Patrick's Day and surround them with water-filled tepees to extend the growing season."

Susan walked me through her attractive garden and pointed out the bounty. Tons of tomato varieties—Roma, Celebrity, Early Girl, Black Plum, Park's Whopper, Heirloom Polish and Heirloom Pineapple Tomatoes. They are tasty; I tried as many varieties as I could. Delicious! Incredible! Fantastic! I'm particularly fond of their heirloom Polish tomatoes. The tomato is firm with a red-pink hue and the flavor is an explosion of juicy sweetness.

They also grow jalapenos, serrano peppers, cucumber, rhubarb, basil as well as a large variety of perennial flowers including datura "Moonflower", sedum, echinacia, hydrangea, butterfly bush, hibiscus, Russian sage, porcupine grass and buffalo grass. They dry, can, and utilize every inch of their garden for the off season. For example, Susan prepares an incredibly healthy Salsa Concentrate made of olive oil, peppers and garlic which she mixes in many dishes year 'round.

Susan and Larry grow much more than they can consume, and they enjoy sharing their bountiful garden produce—both vegetables and flowers—with their neighbors.

Planting a garden in your front yard can be a health solution for many people. The physical activity, daylight exposure, and ability to produce your own organic food are big benefits. If you do not have the perfect location for a garden, follow Susan's determined example to help improve Larry's health and build a garden wherever you possibly can. Be creative, like Susan and Larry, build an incredible vegetable garden in your front yard or on your easement property. If you do not have the space, mix a tomato or two in with your perennial beds or plant a vegetable pot on your balcony. Many communities have public garden areas for your utilization. Call your local city office and ask about renting a plot.

Build a garden in an interesting and unusual space and brighten up your community. What's important is that you get up, get off that couch, and get outside into the natural environment for better health. You can do it!!!

Susan's Famous Healthy Salsa Concentrate

A healthy, vitamin-filled, concentrate Susan Kasprowicz says is easy to make!

Ingredients
- Jalapenos, serranos, or any combination of flavorful chiles to equal 2.5 pounds
- Purified or bottled water (no hard or softened water please)
- Twenty large garlic cloves, peeled
- Kosher or Pickling Salt (no iodized)

De-stem and wash chiles, but leave whole. Place in a stainless steel pan with water just to cover. Bring to a boil and cook about 15 minutes, until chiles are tender. Cool in the water; drain the liquid, but reserve it.

Using the "pulse" function on a food processor or blender, process the whole chiles and peeled garlic until well chopped.

Add pickling or kosher salt to taste (at least a half-teaspoon, for its preservative properties), and stir in reserved chile water to make the consistency of jam.

Store in glass or plastic containers and refrigerate or freeze.

Susan recommends –

Double the recipe if you like. She says it keeps a long time in the refrigerator, but freezing is fine as well.

Susan sometimes freezes ice trays half full of the concentrate and keeps the cubes in a plastic bag to add to soups and stews.

She also adds the concentrate to canned tomatoes, chopped onion, cilantro, and lime juice to make table salsa. You can cook it using canned tomatoes, onion, cider vinegar, and sugar to make a picante; add it to salad dressings and sauces; or make a salsa verde with onions and tomatillos.

The possibilities are endless!

A Garden Can Be Therapy

Therapeutic Landscaping is a relatively new term that is changing the face of traditional landscaping. The term refers to fostering the mental, physical, and spiritual restoration of the human condition in a garden. Therapeutic gardens can be small or large, but all of them encourage total immersion in nature so a person can escape from illness, pain, and depression.

A therapeutic garden can be designed to enhance medical treatments, assist medical staff in giving care, provide relief for a particular medical condition, reduce stress and aggression, or simply provide a place where a busy family can go to heal and relax. A good therapeutic garden is also a green-centered garden, taking advantage of positive environmental practices.

Naomi Sachs, ASLA, is the founder and executive director of the Therapeutic Landscapes Resource Center (TLRC). This not-for-profit organization is dedicated to providing information to the public about restorative landscapes, healing gardens, wellness gardens, and other research-based healthcare landscapes. The Therapeutic Landscapes database provides web-based information and forums with no fee for registration. Sachs' goal is to spread the good word of landscaping for improved health from exposure to nature.

Sachs has been particularly inspired by the effects of the landscaped garden on reducing stress and enhancing creativity. A quote on the TLRC website demonstrates this belief, "Vincent Van Gogh painted his famous 'Iris' series at the

Sanctuary Garden, Santa Fe, NM (2005) Designer: Naomi Sachs Design. Photo by Naomi Sachs

Sanctuary Garden, Santa Fe, NM (2005) Designer: Naomi Sachs Design. Photo by Naomi Sachs

Sachs' walled Sanctuary Garden provides a calm resting place for a stress-centered individual. This garden encourages visitors to be surrounded by calm, peace, and quiet.

Asylum of Saint Paul de Mausole, in Sant-Remy, France, in the spring of 1889. Allowed to roam the asylum's grounds, Van Gogh began painting almost immediately. In a letter to his brother Theo, Van Gogh wrote: '...you will see that considering my life is spent mostly in the garden, it is not so unhappy.' That summer, he wrote, 'For one's health it is necessary to work in the garden and see the flowers growing.'"

Further proof that therapeutic landscape design works comes from research done by Roger Ulrich, Ph.D. of Texas A&M University. He discovered that social support and a sense of control are effective in reduction of stress—thus enhancing lifestyle, medical treatment outcome, and more. Dr. Ulrich believes that exposure to nature and exercise are important to improved health. His research also demonstrates that patients, looking out a window with a garden view, took less pain medication and had shorter hospital stays than those who looked out at a brick wall.

Many designers are beginning to understand the connection Dr. Ulrich has proven between better health and the environment. Naomi Sachs, TLRC founder, has designed many healing gardens through her firm, Naomi Sachs Design. Two of her residential designs touch on improved stress levels and improved exercise benefits. The Sanctuary Garden is a healing place created for a busy, stressed-out business-woman. The owner needed a sanctuary; a place where she could regain her health. The design emphasizes a walled garden to minimize city noise, with softened focal points that allow the eye to rest calmly. The garden requires virtually no upkeep. It is meant to be easy to maintain, simplifying and de-stressing a busy life. The seating area is implicitly simple, providing a place for a cup of tea with breakfast or a quiet moment with a craft.

An octogenarian couple of Santa Fe, New Mexico, Mac and Kay, inspired Sachs design for *Kay's Garden*. For the elderly, declining activity leads to declining health. *Kay's Garden* was built by Sachs to stimulate the couple to get outside and exercise more, thereby improving both their physical and mental health. The previous garden had become weed-filled, inaccessible, and unsuitable for the couple as Kay could no longer venture onto the gravel pathway and stump-strewn terrain. The new garden is easily accessible, includes seating and has a smooth, even walk way to prevent falls.

Seating was important, so Sachs designed a range of seating choices, creating several spaces just off the path where easily movable chairs could be placed for maximum garden enjoyment. Craggy moss-rock boulders were arranged to provide visual interest and catch rainwater where birds and butterflies could drink and bathe. All plants are highly drought tolerant and require little care. Russian sage, catmint, and many grass varieties offer wind-persuaded sound and motion to stimulate the couple's senses. Sachs says, "Plants were chosen for their color, scent, winter interest, and ability to attract wildlife—Mac and Kay are avid birdwatchers." Bird feeders were placed around the garden to invite small birds and animals to come and share the space.

Even before installation was complete, both Kay and Mac started spending an hour or more a day in the garden. Kay began to use the easily navigable walkway for her daily exercise. "Before we created the garden," says Sachs, "Kay did not go outside at all. There was simply no place on the property where she could navigate safely or comfortably."

Only two months later, Kay had become strong enough to walk with Mac up and down the street. The garden brought significant benefits to Mac and Kay, both

Kay's Garden, Santa Fe, New Mexico (2004) Designer: Naomi Sachs Design. Photo by Naomi Sachs

physically and emotionally. This is an amazing example of what a healing garden can become—a delightful spot where an older couple can remain active and healthy, yet still feel safe.

You can create your own therapeutic garden at home. First, you must determine, perhaps with medical consultation, the goal of your garden. It might be to stimulate memories in an Alzheimer's patient or to use medicinal plants in your daily life. Your garden might support healthy outdoor exercise and activity or encourage special needs children to explore. Your design might include a memorial, a healing spot to go to contemplate a friend or family member who has passed on. Another idea is to plant a vegetable garden to provide your own food and improve your diet with fresher foods. Ideas for healthy garden designs are unlimited.

My own garden is definitely therapeutic and was created to bring health to my family and the surrounding community. This ever-expanding creation is filled with perennial beds, as well as smaller outdoor rooms and seating areas. I believe all gardens should have a restful area, where a family can go to release stress, entertain friends, and enjoy each other and nature.

Creating a garden with a special purpose is a great way to encourage better health for you and your family. I hope you find a special spot in your yard or on your property which can become a healing resource for you.

Shawna designed this relaxing garden to encourage her family to get away from stress and enjoy nature.

Part II—
Green and Simple
Conservation Plan

---

*"When we heal the earth,
we heal ourselves."*

—DR. DAVID ORR, PROFESSOR OF ENVIRONMENTAL STUDIES
AND POLITICS AND CHAIR OF THE ENVIRONMENTAL
STUDIES PROGRAM AT OBERLIN COLLEGE.

D	#	S	A	V	E	#	A
N	!	T	1	B	2	%	#
A	X	H	W	R	?	3	L
#	H	E	O	E	9	:	I
E	E	%	R	A	6	4	F
E	L	8	L	T	!	&	E
R	P	?	D	H	7	5	#
T	#	A	#	E	V	A	S

Chapter Six

Green and Simple Conservation Plan

∞

An integral part of the *Get Your Green On Healthy Philosophy* is the Green and Simple Conservation Plan. It offers eleven easy-to-do ideas to get you started toward a greener lifestyle. This plan shows you how to improve your home and garden, your health and our world by helping our natural environment.

Practicing home conservation means you can save hundreds, sometimes thousands, of dollars every year in utility bills. By practicing conservation, while you are saving money, you also save the earth and get healthier. There is much more to conservation than simply conserving water or electricity. Conservation is also about saving our land, and the precious life and natural resources on that land. It is practicing safety by utilizing chemicals that are better for the environment and safer for humans. Ultimately, it is taking responsibility for yourself and your family's ecological footprint on our planet.

My syndicated "green" advice column, *The Casual Gardener*, speaks to many green concerns. The below column ran when a friend sent me an email saying how overwhelmed and hopeless she feels when looking at the "big picture" of conservation on a global scale:

> Dear Casual Gardener,
>
> I want to get started healthy gardening or volunteering in my community to improve the environment, but I don't know how I'd be considered qualified! I can't get my family to recycle. I don't do chemical-free yard maintenance. I eat at fast food restaurants that devastate the rain forests. I don't drive a bio-diesel car. My house isn't on any type of sustainable power. Right now I'm drinking from a Styrofoam cup, using a plastic spoon for my too-much-packaging yogurt. I had non-free-trade coffee on my way in to work. I'm going through reams of paper with my incessant printing. My clothes are made in third world country sweat shops. The meat I buy at the grocery store is from animals that decimate our country's rivers and streams. The vegetables and fruit at the store come from other countries!
>
> My ecological footprint is an embarrassment to myself and to everything I believe in. I would feel like a complete hypocrite to try to point anyone in the right direction on ecology or a healthy world!!!
>
> Signed, Mary, Aurora, Illinois

= = = = = = = = = =

Dear Mary,

WHOA—slow down—you are not an environmental hypocrite. You need to take *baby steps*! To begin, you should take one step at a time. Before you perfect your ecological footprint, remember that every positive change starts with a single person who cares.

I bet there is some group in your town that could truly use a volunteer once a month. That is doable and not too hard. It doesn't significantly change your ecological footprint, but it does get you started learning more about how to get yourself and your community healthy. Contact your local city government or chamber of commerce and ask for help! The organizations with which I volunteer are desperate for people to come and help. There will be a place you will fit in which will help you get started.

Gardening is how I began, it has made me healthier. I know a lot more about nature, and it has introduced me to the global gardening and environmental community where I continually learn more ways to accomplish positive environmental practices. My eco-footprint is far from perfect, but it is coming along with gradual improvement.

Remember— keep it simple to start! By taking baby steps and learning as you go, you will soon be inspiring others to do important work which will be good for our world.

Below is a famous quote from Harriet Tubman—a woman born into slavery, who was an abolitionist and the leader of the Underground Railroad. She dedicated her life to freeing slaves and became an integral part in American history by inspiring millions. She took on a monumental task, which seemed totally impossible at the time, by accomplishing goals, one step at a time. Harriet says, "*Every great dream begins with a dreamer. Always remember, you have within you the strength, the patience, and the passion to reach for the stars to change the world.* "

Let Harriet Tubman inspire you to get started, one step at a time, to accomplish the task of achieving a healthier stress-reduced existence!

My reader's frustration is understandable. There seems to be too much to learn and too much to keep up with to be environmentally friendly. Mary was not the only reader who came to me for help, I often hear comments like, "I try to recycle, but I'm not very good at it." Or, "It's not my fault that the landfills are overfilled." Or, "Why should I reduce carbon emissions when giant factories are spewing out 100 times what my little car produces?" We all must get past the negative attitude about participating in a greener lifestyle because we *are* responsible. Your local ecological footprint is strongly influenced by the way you practice conservation.

You would not put a trash dump on your front lawn, stinking and steaming, for the rest of the neighbors to look at. Beyond looking bad, you could also leech chemicals into the neighborhood and cause harm. You know this because the media has taught you what type of harm dumps in your neighborhood can do. The truth is that living in the modern world produces by-products from garbage to chemical fumes. The garbage you produce, the electricity you consume, the water table you destroy with chemicals—these things cannot be seen sitting on your front lawn, but all are still your responsibility because you affect them *directly*.

At the beginning of this book, I share a conversation with Stacey, a friend of mine who wants health help. One thing I point out to her is that by being more responsible and by taking care of others—our family, our community, and our planet—we will feel more emotionally connected and healthier. Taking care of nature often involves caring for trees, plants, and water much as you would a pet. This is an *emotionally healing* activity. The natural world needs you. It is the garden right outside your front door as well as the air someone is breathing half-way around the world. On a larger scale, frequently what we do here in the United States affects our neighboring countries. The earth, like your body, is a system. We are all connected. Practicing conservation and greening is taking a step towards emotional and physical responsibility. It is being healthy.

Some people refuse to go green because they feel completely overwhelmed, as if their effort is futile. For every carbon emission you might save, there is a huge company out there sending more into the air. Yet, compare it to the infamous Aesop's Fable; "The Tortoise and The Hare." The tortoise, although slow, plods along one step at a time, eating away the miles, and eventually wins the race because of his persistence. You can be persistent when building a conservation plan for yourself and your family.

Frequently, I hear this ecological theme: "Think Global, Act Local." Without a doubt, we need to see the global picture. However, we cannot fight the miles of overwhelming global issues directly, we must attack the issues as the tortoise has, one step at a time. Through persistence, we will cover the miles and eventually conquer the unhealthy habits we have all developed.

Many diseases and illnesses are exacerbated by pollution. Pediatric asthma, for instance, has grown significantly in the last ten years. Families who live close to large cities or near heavy air pollution have higher incidences of asthma, allergy, cancer, and other health concerns.

Allergies, according to government statistics, cost Americans approximately $11 billion in 2005. This includes a variety of treatments including doctor's visits and prescription drug medications. These statistics do not include over-the-counter medication expenditures. Every year these numbers rise. There are many theories on why Americans suffer more every year from allergy symptoms, chief among these theories is the increasing level of air pollution. Wouldn't it be amazing if you could contribute to the reduction of human suffering in the world by beginning your own conservation plan and reducing the amount of air, water, and land pollution your family generates?

Maybe you could inspire others in your community to begin their own conservation changes. Then all of you could come together for the greater good to demand your city, county, or state pass effective laws to protect your family and community. Perhaps you can get those large factories to stop polluting if you band together as a community. Alone and isolated, we sometimes feel impotent; but united as a team, we can accomplish impossible tasks.

The truth is apparent—one person *can* make a difference. You can make a difference by modeling a good conservation plan for your neighbors and community. More important, you can make a difference by showing your children and family how they can practice conservation. When they grow up, they will remember what you taught them. They will make a difference for their families. Your inspiration, by setting a responsible example, will spread and touch many. Think big, but start small at home, practicing conservation one step at a time.

Conservation is doing the right thing, doing the healthy thing. Just take that first step.

Green and Simple Conservation Plan:

- Recycle! Recycling or reusing trash prevents increased landfill usage and community water problems.

- Buy recycled products to promote more recycling.

- Conserve water with of rain barrels, rain gardens, reduced usage, mulching and improved watering systems.

- Compost natural waste instead of throwing it away.

- Use perennials and native plantings in your yard to conserve water, soil, and attract beneficial wildlife.

- Buy at local farmers' markets and participate in food co-ops that purchase locally grown produce.

- Use non-chemical solutions on your property.

- Save money by reducing natural resource usage such as electric and gas utilities in your home.

- Use Compact Fluorescent Light (CFL) bulbs.

- Promote stewardship of the land by removing invasive species, chemical waste dumps, and garbage.

- Participate in community outreach programs for conservation.

Chapter Seven

Strip Away The Excuses—How To Make The Conservation Plan A Reality

∞

When you practice home conservation, you feel good because you are caring for the earth and for your community. Begin simply; one task, one step and one day at a time. You *can* make a difference. Mother Teresa of Calcutta won the Nobel Prize for Peace in 1979. She accomplished enormous tasks, inspired world leaders and people of all religions and ethnicities. She said, "I never look at the masses as my responsibility; I look at the individual. I can only love one person at a time—just one, one, one. So you begin. I began— I picked up one person. Maybe if I didn't pick up that one person, I wouldn't have picked up forty-two thousand… The same thing goes for you, the same thing in your family, the same thing in your church, your community. Just begin— one, one, one."

How insightful Mother Teresa was. She understood that looking at the big picture can be a frightening experience, while viewing the world with a narrower, more insightful gaze can help everyone accomplish more. This is excellent inspiration to help you think global, act local.

There are many ways to get started with a simple conservation plan at home. The eleven ideas here are the backbone of the Green and Simple Conservation Plan and should be a starting point for you and your family to get involved in being healthier and greener.

After reviewing these steps, write a short list of items you and your family would like to adopt immediately. Children are often catalysts for conservation plans. They are encouraged and excited to know that they are helping the world. This beginning will seem like a small step towards the "Think Global, Act Local" concept; however, in reality, it is a huge step for our environment. Get started now!

Step One   **Recycle! Recycling or reusing trash prevents increased landfill usage and community water problems.**

There are many important reasons to recycle, but the most important reason is it saves natural resources. By reusing or making products from recycled materials instead of virgin materials, we save money and energy. The United States Environmental Protection Agency says recycling IS working on a national basis and is encouraging all communities to have a recycling program.

In most cases, recycling saves energy as it takes less energy to make recycled products versus producing products from raw materials. It takes 95 percent less energy to make new aluminum products from recycled aluminum and soda cans than from new aluminum ore.

International symbol for recycling.

According to the Carnegie Mellon Green Practices (CMGP) website, 77 percent of paper waste generated in offices is recyclable. Making new paper products from old paper uses between 30 and 55 percent less energy than making paper from trees. Related air pollution is reduced by 95 percent.

The CMGP website lists these statistics for resources which are saved by each ton of recycled paper:

- 17 trees
- 275 pounds of sulphur
- 350 pounds of limestone
- 9,000 pounds of steam
- 60,000 gallons of water
- 225 kilowatt hours
- 3.3 cubic yards of landfill space

Recycling saves landfill space. The United States is quickly running out of landfill space. Recycling one ton of paper saves approximately six cubic yards of landfill space. On average one cubic yard of stacked paper weighs 380 pounds.

The process of recycling creates jobs and is typically the least expensive waste management method for cities and towns. Newspaper, for instance can be recycled into more newspaper, game boards, egg cartons, gift boxes, packaging material, and much more. This touches on multiple businesses beyond the recycling industry. By looking at the bigger picture, you can see how recycling touches thousands of lives in a positive way.

Recycling has its problems. The on going confusion over what we can or cannot recycle can be confounding. To begin, there is glass, paper, metal, paint, battery, appliance, and plastic recycling. Thirty-nine states now require that the symbol code we are familiar with for plastics be placed on almost all plastic products. It is a single digit ranging from 1 to 7 and surrounded by a triangle of arrows designed by The Society of the Plastic Industry (SPI) in 1988. However, this symbol doesn't always mean that the city or county you live in accepts this particular type of recycling product.

Check with your local city or county to see what recycling products they take and start recycling immediately. Often, recycling is picked up with the garbage. When it is not, most counties have a recycling center which accepts drop-offs. Start recycling today for a cleaner world.

Step Two **Buy recycled products to help promote more recycling**

Buying recycled products is easy. Almost everyone owns at least one antique purchased from a garage sale or antiques shop. Antiques are sometimes far more beautiful than brand new and you are reusing products which were owned by another individual. Vintage or resale shops sell used clothing, often in excellent condition and at a much reduced cost.

Handmade papers and stationery are often recycled newspaper and copy paper. Read the labels and you will discover many recycled products. Indeed, we have become a nation of label readers. We have to—it is important—due to the large number of chemicals and processing procedures our food and commercial products go through.

This photo shows a used clothing store in Shawna's community. Profits go to a local non-profit agency which sponsors youth and family services within the community.

Buying recycled involves occasionally reading a label to identify the type of recycled product you are purchasing. Understanding which is which will help distinguish your purchase. For example, recycled-content products are made from materials that would have been thrown away during the manufacturing process or industrial activity. These items are made partially, sometimes totally, from recovered material. Recycled-content products can also be items that are rebuilt for reuse, such as toner cartridges and computers. If a product you are purchasing is labeled "recycled content", this does not mean the material came from a local recycling program.

There are several types of papers out there: virgin wood fiber, pre-consumer waste or post-consumer waste. Distinguishing between them is important when purchasing recycled products. Virgin wood has zero recycled content. Pre-consumer content paper is made from scraps and trimmings left over from the normal paper manufacturing process. Post-consumer waste products are created from material that was directly used by a consumers or businesses and would have been discarded as waste, such as tin and aluminum cans, soda-pop bottles, tires, or old clothing. The preferred choice is to buy paper which is 100 percent post-consumer.

Recyclable products can be remanufactured into new products if they are disposed of at the proper recycling facility. Do not be fooled into thinking these products have already been recycled or made from recycled material. Read those labels to find out more about buying recycled products.

Step Three   **Conserve water with rain barrels, rain gardens, reduced usage, mulching and improved watering systems.**

Using water wisely has become critical. If water is constantly being cleaned and recycled through the earth's water cycle, why do we need to conserve it? The answer is that people use up our planet's freshwater faster than it can naturally be replenished. Nearly three-quarters of our planet is covered by water; yet, only 1 to 2 percent supports our earth's life.

Growing industrial and residential demand, proliferation of urban sprawl, wasteful agribusiness consumption, and industrial poisoning of existing community wells are draining our reservoirs and straining water treatment, distribution, and disposal systems. As water is stolen from rivers and streams, the amount of sand that accumulates on beaches also diminishes, threatening the health of vital coastal wetlands and wildlife.

Already, in the United States, many cities are under a constant drought warning. Al Gore writes in his book, *An Inconvenient Truth,* about the environmental cost of river diversion for irrigation purposes. Related to this subject, global and climate changes, such as flooding, droughts, and extreme weather events, are also making freshwater increasingly scarce on a global level.

Taking advantage of natural sources for water, therefore, becomes important both to you individually and to the community in which you live. Reducing the water you utilize on your property and reusing water whenever possible are the first steps to conserving. Reducing water usage clearly saves money as well. Follow some of these techniques to reduce water consumption:

- Stop letting the water run when you brush your teeth.
- Install a water-conserving toilet flushing mechanism.
- Install low flow showerheads.
- Purchase water-saving clothes washing machines and dishwashers.
- Fill the sink basin when shaving and doing dishes.
- Landscape your property utilizing native and drought-tolerant plants.
- Avoid spraying your driveway and sidewalks with water; use a broom instead.
- Use rain barrels, rain gardens, improved watering systems, and mulching techniques in your garden.

Warrenville, Illinois became the first community in the Midwest to use permeable brick pavers on a public road. Phase I implementation began in 2007 with current expectations of completion of further phases in 2009.

Rain is free, and is the easiest water to collect and reuse. Some progress in our country with new technology includes green roofs and

An easy to install rain barrel.

permeable paver roads and parking lots which allow water to drain back into the water table instead of being diverted to rivers and pulled away from local communities. However, most water which falls as rain from the sky is not captured for reuse. Imagine every American taking advantage of this free resource by collecting it right in their own backyards! Sounds easy, doesn't it?

Rain barrels and cisterns that collect water which comes off your roof can be purchased readily online and at lawn and garden centers. They hold the water to water your garden and lawn and are particularly helpful during drought. Depending upon yearly rainfall in your area, it is possible to collect about half a gallon of water for each square foot of roof space from one inch of rainfall. That is a lot of water to save!

A rain garden is a man-made depression in the ground built to hold water run-off and can be used on residential, commercial and industrial properties. It improves water quality while beautifying your landscape. A rain garden forms a "bioretention area" by collecting water runoff, storing it, then permitting it to be filtered through and slowly absorbed by the soil. The idea is based on the hydrologic function of forest habitat in which the forest produces a spongy litter layer that soaks up water and allows it to slowly penetrate the soil layer.

A nutrient filtering process takes place when the water comes in contact with soil, roots, shrubs, and vegetation. This process accounts for improved water quality in the water table. The first flush of rain water is held in the depression of the rain garden, and contains the highest concentration of materials washed off impervious surfaces such as roofs, roads, and parking lots.

Using proper water conservation techniques is critical for a good garden. To water correctly, soak the ground infrequently, yet deeply, at the root level. Frequent light sprinklings can do more harm than good and wastes a lot of water. You are saving water by watering as closely to the roots as possible. Watering in the early morning or late evening reduces water evaporation significantly. Adding organic matter before planting, such as compost or pine bark soil conditioner, helps retain moisture when the soil begins to dry out. Loosening and aerating the soil also enables the plants to develop a more extensive root system.

Proper garden mulching is important to water conservation. A layer of mulch not only helps maintain moisture, it also reduces weeds. The best choice for shrubbery beds is usually two to four inches of shredded mulch or pine

Rain barrel system for more than one rain barrel installation.

needles. For flower beds two to three inches is good. In the vegetable garden, mulching options include three layers of newspaper, straw, chopped leaves, or even recycled products like carpeting and cardboard. Also, mulch the lawn by utilizing a mulching lawnmower. Leaving a thin layer of grass clippings on the lawn is good, if you do not let it get too thick. The recycled clippings act as a mulch and help to reduce weeds and maintain moisture, while at the same time, recycle nutrients.

Along with proper mulching, a good plan is to establish "water use zones" in your landscape. This can save you a tremendous

Mulch provides strong protection against drought.

watering cost. Group plants together according to their watering needs. Group all the plants that need the most water, separated from those that require little water. Drip irrigation also saves on water as it prevents a high water evaporation rate.

When it comes to garden pots, I have a favorite water-saving trick. Many people water garden pots daily as most annual plants demand high moisture. I mix a heavy dose of polymer water crystals into the potting soil for all of my pots.

These super absorbent polymers can release up to 95 percent of the water absorbed and make it available to the plant, using far less water over a week's time. Approximately one pound of polymer crystals can absorb and hold between thirty and forty-seven gallons of water. With the crystals added, I only water once or twice a week, dependent on heat exposure.

Install drip irrigation hose for the best water saving irrigation.

| Step Four | Compost natural waste instead of throwing it away. |

Food scraps and yard clippings make up one quarter of the United States' solid waste piling up in landfills. The book, *True Green*, says, "When this organic matter ends up in landfills and decomposes without air, it produces methane, a greenhouse gas twenty times more potent than carbon dioxide."

Composting is the way to cleanly convert kitchen and garden waste into productive soil matter and it is one of nature's best mulches and soil amendments. You can make it without spending a cent, which helps save you money. Using compost improves soil structure, texture, aeration, and increases the soil's water-holding capacity. Compost loosens clay soils and helps sandy soils retain water. Adding compost improves soil fertility and stimulates healthy root development in plants. The organic matter in compost provides food for microorganisms, which keeps the soil in a healthy, balanced condition. Nitrogen, potassium, and phosphorus are produced naturally by these microorganisms, so few if any soil amendments need to be added once you use compost.

Compost is the end product of a complex feeding pattern involving hundreds of different organisms, including bacteria, fungi, worms, and insects. The goal is to produce a humus-like material which replicate's the nutrient rich forest floor. Almost any organic material is

Simple compost bin which has been made from recycling shipping pallets.

suitable for a compost pile. The pile needs a proper ratio of carbon-rich materials, or "browns," and nitrogen-rich materials, or "greens," and moisture. Below is a list of browns and greens you might use in your compost pile.

Examples of browns:
• Newspaper, black-and-white print preferred.
• Brown paper bags from the grocery store.
• Shredded cardboard.
• Cotton and paper-based tissues and towels.
• Shredded cotton clothes.
• Floor sweepings.
• Aged sawdust from untreated lumber.
• Straw.
• Aged grass clippings.
• Dead leaves. Do not use dead leaves from diseased plants.

Examples of greens:
• New grass clippings.
• Plant prunings. Do not add prunings from diseased plants.
• Spent flowers and pulled weeds.
• Coffee grounds.
• Tea bags with metal staple removed.
• Kitchen scraps. Avoid items that will root, such as potato skins and onions, unless ground completely.
• Barnyard animal manures such as cow, horse, chicken, goat, sheep, and rabbit. Do not use dog, cat, or human manure/feces as they may contain pathogens or diseases that could be harmful.

Managed composting involves active participation, including turning the pile occasionally. On average, it takes between three and four weeks to create compost. The speed is determined by the products you add, if they are chopped up, and how often you turn the pile. A good balance of carbon and nitrogen encourages quicker composting.

The temperature of the managed pile is important—it indicates the activity of the decomposition process. It should be warm or hot to the touch. If it is not, then the microbial activity has slowed down and you need to add more green materials. This heat can be encouraged if you place your compost pile in full sun.

Keeping the pile moist is also important as organic waste needs water to decompose. Gray water, in other words, old dish water or clothes washer water from your home can be drained into a compost pile regularly. The rule of thumb is to keep the pile as moist as a wrung-out sponge. If you actively manage the composting, within a few weeks you will have a rich additive for your garden which cost you nothing.

| Step Five | Use perennials and native plantings in your yard to conserve water, soil and attract beneficial wildlife. |

Perennial plants and native plantings typically offer many water-saving and soil advantage. They also encourage local, native animals as these animals have evolved with native plants. The animals require natives for food and shelter. Planting these types of plants can be the best way to attract butterflies and birds to enjoy. By encouraging native plantings of shrubs and perennials, you encourage habitat renewal.

Drought tolerant flower, Black-eyed susan, in full bloom.

Non-natives often guzzle far more water than natives. To save water, prepare the soil with water conserving amendments and use natives or create an interesting mix of natives and drought tolerant plantings. According to *True Green*, "growing indigenous plants can save 50 percent of the water typically used to maintain outdoor plants." Native plants are amazingly diverse and vary significantly from state to state. To find a native plantings list for your area, inquire at local nurseries, local cooperative extension programs, or gardening clubs.

Russian Sage mixed with wildflowers.

Common drought tolerant perennials are easy to find and well labeled at nurseries and home centers. Many drought tolerant perennials will work from zones three to nine in the United States. All plants, even cacti, need some level of water and light exposure, so be sure to investigate which drought tolerant plants work best in your planting area. Always be sure to read and follow planting labels carefully. My top ten long flowering favorites are listed below:

Common Drought Tolerant Perennials

Black-eyed susan (*Rudbeckia fulgida sullivantii goldsturm*)
Blanket flower (*Gaillardia*)—any variety
Creeping phlox (*Phlox subulata*)
Coneflower (*Echinacea*)—any variety
Coreopsis (*Coreopsis*)—any variety
Lamb's ears (*Stachys byzantina*)
Penstemon (*Penstemon*)—any variety
Russian sage (*Perovskia atriplicifolia*)
Stone crop (*Sedum*)—any variety
Yarrow (*Achillea*)—any variety

Step Six   **Buy at local farmers' markets and participate in food co-ops that purchase locally grown produce.**

By purchasing more food products which are locally produced, you increase regional economic health as well as your own health. In other words, you are keeping money within the community and encouraging economic growth for you and your neighbors.

When you buy locally produced foods, you get more nutritious, fresher, and flavorful foods. Such foods are likely to have been harvested within the week, or even within twenty-four hours. Produce picked at the height of freshness tastes better, has more vitamins, and is more nutritionally complete. Nutritional value declines dramatically as time passes after harvesting.

Locally produced foods also require significantly less energy consumption compared with products from growing areas all over the world. The required transportation and storage consumes large amounts of energy and pollutes the world's air and water.

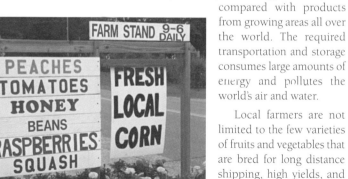

Local farmers are not limited to the few varieties of fruits and vegetables that are bred for long distance shipping, high yields, and exceptionally long shelf life. Our local farmers often help preserve biodiversity by raising and selling heirloom varieties. These vari-

Farm stand sign featuring fresh fruits, vegetables, and honey.

eties are almost im-
possible to find in
large supermarkets,
and are far more fla-
vorful and nutritious
than standard vari-
eties.

Another important
feature—farmers do
not need to use as
many waxes or
fungicide applications
to protect their
harvest compared

Tomato farm stand filled to overflowing with fresh tomatoes of every variety.

with those traveling long distances or stored over long periods. This reduces the
amount of chemicals to which you and your family are exposed. Organic foods
which have been grown without added chemicals are far healthier for you,
however, it is equally important to purchase local produce whenever possible to
prevent further ecological devastation of our natural environment.

You can buy local at farmers' stands and now many grocers are supplied by
regional farmers. Inquire at your local grocer to find out where the food comes
from. Another way to buy local is to participate in a food cooperative. A food co-
op is a group of local farmers that have come together to form a grocery store. It
is usually owned and paid for by participating consumers who are members of the
organization. Benefits of a food co-op community extend far beyond the aisles of
groceries. It is intimately tied to the health of the local economy. Food co-ops are
places where social capital and community are built and sustained.

To find a local food co-op contact your local government, cooperative
horticulture extension office, environmental agency, or search for a directory
online.

Step Seven   Use non-chemical solutions on your property.

Every day Americans are exposed to hundreds of chemicals and chemical fumes.
These toxic chemicals are found everywhere, from exposure to computer, printer,
and carpet fumes in our homes to driving on exhaust-filled roadways to walking
down the detergent and cleaning aisle at the grocery store. Chemical exposure is
also prevalent indoors at schools, office buildings, shopping centers, and your
own home. This regular exposure increases our sensitivity and, in repeated
studies, has been shown to cause many health problems.

Air quality is a serious concern, particularly to children. University of Texas
Southwestern Medical Center is a top research institution focused on finding ways
to reduce the severity and frequency of asthma attacks in inner-city children.
Dr. Rebecca Gruchalla, chief of allergy at UT Southwestern, said, "Children living

in inner cities are exposed to higher allergen levels and tend to have more severe asthma than children living elsewhere."

With industrial pollution, mosquito spraying, idling cars in common areas, and many other air quality issues now a major concern in the United States, we must all be aware of the air quality where we live and work to improve it. Indoor toxicity of all types are of immediate concern to you and your health. You can easily reduce the amount of chemicals you use indoors which affect the health of your family by reading labels and purchasing non-toxic solutions.

Fumes from idling cars near schools and in large cities contribute to the growing asthma and illness rate. In addition, idling cars waste gasoline resources. Turn off your car and help improve your community's air quality.

Toxic chemicals used outdoors affect your entire community. This is why using chemicals on your outdoor plants is a particular concern. A study done by Virginia Tech states Virginians use nearly 400 million gallons of groundwater each day to address the needs of industrial, agricultural, public and private water demands. Many in Virginia depend on groundwater as their primary source for fresh drinking water. According to the Virginia Tech Cooperative Extension group, there is a direct connection between groundwater contamination and chemical use on lawns, fields and gardens within the state of Virginia.

The groundwater percolation process begins when water and chemicals enter the soil by rainfall or irrigation. Gradually, the liquids percolate downward to become groundwater. The geologic formation through which groundwater moves is called an aquifer and can supply water for thousands of families. The percolation process can take a long time as groundwater moves very slowly, only a few feet a month or even a year. Chemical toxicity can be detected years from the original contamination date and can make the water unusable. It might take many decades for a contaminant to be naturally diluted, so prevention of groundwater contamination is extremely important.

To live in a cleaner environment, we need to stop using toxic chemicals on our lawns and in our environment right now. Expand garden beds and eliminate or reduce contaminating lawn-care chemicals as much as you can.

Creating a less toxic environment, both indoors and outdoors, will help you lead a greener life. To simplify this task, search for non-toxic solutions whenever possible to improve air and water quality for everyone.

Step Eight	**Save money by reducing electric and gas usage in your home so natural resources will not be used and wasted to bring these products to your home.**

This is easy—you want to save money? Turn off the lights! Conserving energy in your home helps preserve natural resources and reduces the impact energy use has on the environment.

There are many easy tips to reduce energy, such as turning off unused lights when you are not in the room. Make sure registers are not blocked and vents and radiator valves are closed in unused rooms is a great way to prevent energy leeching as well.

The largest user of energy in your home is your heating and cooling system. Research and purchase the best, most energy-efficient system. Locate the thermostat on an inside wall away from windows and doors to avoid cold drafts that can keep the system running even when the rest of the house is warm.

In winter turn the thermostat down as low as you can. Each degree above sixty-eight degrees Fahrenheit adds 3 percent to the amount of energy needed for heating. Also, use kitchen and bath exhaust fans sparingly in the winter to keep as much heat as possible inside your house. In the heating season, water vapors from bathing and cooking are beneficial because they help humidify the home.

In summer, set your thermostat to seventy-eight degrees Fahrenheit, or as high as comfort permits. Close your blinds and curtains during the day, particularly where sun directly filters through windows. Clean filters monthly and condense coils yearly. Close cooling vents in unused rooms. Reduce your air-conditioning usage by 10 to 20 percent by caulking and weather-stripping doors and windows. Insulate your house well to prevent air leakage and temperature fluctuations.

Another large energy user is your hot water system. Reduce your water heating bill 10 percent by lowering the water heater temperature. Once a year, drain a bucket of water from the bottom of the water heater tank. This gets rid of sediment, which can waste energy by blocking up the water in the tank from the heating element. Consider a water heater insulation kit, which reduces the amount of heat lost through the walls of the tank.

As you move to energy-efficient appliances you will notice considerable savings to your utility bill bottom line. Remember, saving energy and natural resources, in this case, saves you money.

Step Nine   Use compact fluorescent light (CFL) bulbs.

Following moves already made by Australia and Europe, the United States has passed an energy bill that, among other things, bans the sale of the hugely inefficient incandescent light bulb after 2012. That makes the best choice currently, from an energy savings perspective, the compact fluorescent light bulb. Using CFLs in fixtures that are on for more than two hours a day makes energy sense. CFLs give the same warm, soft light of an incandescent bulb, while using up to 75 percent less electricity. They also last about ten times longer.

To reduce your electricity bill and be more energy-conscious, it is definitely time to follow this bright idea and convert all of your household bulbs.

CFLs do have one problem. You should not dispose of broken or used CFLs in your trash or burn them in an incinerator because they contain a small percentage, approximately five milligrams, of mercury. Energy Star, the Environmental Protection Agency (EPA) and U.S. Department of Energy's joint energy savings program, recommends consumers recycle fluorescent light bulbs using available facilities. The EPA is currently working with CFL manufacturing companies and retailers to expand the disposal and recycling programs.

Also, if you purchase an Energy Star qualified CFL, the CFL will be covered under a warranty. If the bulb has fails within the warranty period, return it to your retailer.

Step Ten   **Promote stewardship of the land by removing invasive species, chemical waste dumps, and garbage.**

According to the team at The Conservation Foundation in DuPage County, Illinois, practicing stewardship and preserving open space, both on public and private land, is one of the best ways to preserve the quality of community life. I strongly believe this is true. Keeping a cleaner environment where we live also promotes our personal good health.

The Conservation Foundation works to educate consumers on problems associated with stewardship. For example, many invasive plant species have attacked our neighborhood communities. Invasive species are defined as species that are non-native to the local ecosystem. The invasive introductions often cause harm to the economy, environment, and to human health. Invasive species can be plants, animals, or other organisms, such as microbes. While most invasive species were introduced to the United States, some are natives in one part of the country

Working tirelessly to promote better environmental care, the team at The Conservation Foundation have really made a difference by educating the community in the Midwest on proper land stewardship. (photo courtesy of The Conservation Foundation)

but serious pests in another. In addition, there are problem plants that are native but invade managed habitats, such as rangelands or agricultural fields.

Invasive species threaten native plants, animals, and ecosystems. They also impact agricultural ecosystems and other human activity. Control costs and environmental damages can add up to millions of dollars per year. Purple loosestrife is an example of a plant that competes highly with native species. In the 1800's, this wetland flower was introduced for ornamental and medicinal purposes. Since then, it has invaded wetlands across much of the nation. Purple loosestrife forms dense stands that replace native plants needed by wildlife for food and habitat. It also causes millions of dollars of damage by clogging waterways.

Removing invasive species on your property is a critical part of personal land stewardship. Cleaning up chemicals and garbage is also important. Chemical waste is defined as the waste created from harmful chemicals. This could be as simple as leaving a leaky bleach or cleaning-chemical container out behind the garage or as complicated as having nuclear waste somewhere on your property. The hazards posed by chemicals for children, plants, and animals can be deadly—be a good steward and take care of the environment properly by dumping your chemicals and garbage in an appropriate facility.

One of the days we celebrate land stewardship is on April 22, which is Earth Day. On Earth Day, 2002, President Bush said, "Good stewardship is a personal responsibility of all of us. And it's a public value. And that's what's important for Americans to understand, that each of us have a responsibility, and it's a part of our value system in our country to assume that responsibility." This quote sums up the reality of how we should move forward with land stewardship. We must value and take care of our property, land, and nature so we all can enjoy it together.

Beyond your personal property, there is also a concern for public property and our waterways. Many dump pharmaceuticals, chemicals and garbage in our rivers by route of storm drains. This has become such a large concern that the EPA has created a national guideline for it. "Dump No Waste—Drains To River" stencils are available through the EPA. This is a fantastic community improvement project idea—to bring members of your community together in stenciling teams to improve land and water stewardship and prevent further chemical poisoning of our communities.

The first Earth Day was on April 22, 1970. It was founded by Senator Gaylord Nelson who saw a lack of environmental concern at the political level and wanted to make a difference. Earth Day turned out to be a marvelous tool to educate public and political organizations on promoting stewardship and encouraging community participation. Senator

Nelson said, "Earth Day worked because of the spontaneous response at the grassroots level. We had neither the time nor resources to organize 20 million demonstrators and the thousands of schools and local communities that participated. That was the remarkable thing about Earth Day. It organized itself."

In my mind, Earth Day organized itself because people fundamentally knew it was important to care about their communities. I want this caring to proliferate throughout our society, to motivate people in all our communities worldwide to take care of our Earth.

Step Eleven	Participate in community outreach programs for conservation.

Community involvement is at the heart of building a strong and responsive conservation effort. Thousands of communities throughout the United States have programs that utilize volunteers to encourage conservation and build better, cleaner communities. The current greening effort has put a spurt in the proliferation of environmental and conservation organizations, both national and local.

Thirteen thousand environmental organizations are listed in the National Environmental Directory, available online at www.environmnetaldirectory.net. The list includes hundreds of national organizations, many with local chapters, such as the National Wildlife Federation, Audubon Society and the Izaak Walton League. Better yet, it also lists regional and local organizations. This is an exceptionally good resource for connecting to groups in your community.

In some large communities, environmental and conservation groups have connected to form an umbrella organization. The Chicago Wilderness Consortium, an alliance of more than 200 private and public organizations, joined to unify their work in protecting Chicagoland's natural lands, plants, and animals. Thousands of volunteers in these member organizations study, protect, manage, and restore the region's natural heritage. Their website says, "The consortiums' mission is to restore the region's natural community to long-term viability, enrich local residents' quality of life and contribute to the preservation of global diversity."

Personally, I am involved, or have been involved previously, in several groups within my community, and each is rewarding in its own way. I have been the chairperson for the Environmental Advisory Commission for my city, which was an immensely enriching and educational experience. The Board of Directors for Fermilab National Accelerator Laboratory's Natural Areas has me serve as an officer. Also, I am a member of the local America In Bloom chapter, an initiative that strongly encourages conservation, environmental efforts, and land stewardship.

Making conservation and environmentally-related changes within city government, or for government facilities is a slow and tedious process; but when change happen, it is very rewarding.

As you can see, I have listed eleven steps to help you get started with a healthy conservation plan for your family. They are all simple to do, but take effort. Of course, you cannot do all of these ideas in one day or even in one week. In fact, you will more effectively change your lifestyle if you gradually green. Incorporating more greening and conservation ideas needs to be an ongoing effort. You will feel good emotionally by helping your community. In addition, many of these greening ideas include aspects of doing good things for your health as they include physical exercise and daylight exposure.

An abbreviated list of my top twenty favorite conservation ideas is below. It gives you a quick list of things you can apply immediately in your quest for a greener life. These ideas are very easy to do and can reduce the amount of money spent yearly on utilities as well:

1. Install low-flow shower fittings to save water. Some families save more than 20,000 gallons of water per year by making this change.

2. Turn unused lights and appliances off to reduce electricity usage.

3. Turn the heat or air conditioning down in your home to reduce emissions and save money.

4. Unplug electronic equipment and appliances when not in use to prevent energy leeching.

5. Replace all light bulbs with compact fluorescent light bulbs.

6. Use fewer chemicals on your property. When necessary, try to use chemicals and cleaners which are certified safe for the environment.

7. Utilize native plants or drought tolerant plants in your garden to save water.

8. Plant at least one tree a year. Effectively planted trees cool your home in summer and allow sunlight to warm your home in the winter.

9. Use rain barrels to collect rainfall from your downspout. You can collect as much as 36,000 gallons of rainwater each year from a 2,000-square-foot home.

10. Water as closely to the roots of your plants as possible to save water. Reducing water evaporation by watering in the early morning or late evening will also help conserve.

11. Mulch gardens to keep the ground cool and moist for more water savings.

12. Encourage birds, butterflies and nature by planting bushes and plants which encourage food and nesting locations.

13. Use a rake or broom to clear off the lawn and sidewalk. Hosing and power washing wastes water.

14. Grow your own fruits and vegetables or buy local produce for better nutrition and less transportation energy waste.

15. Prevent landfill waste by creating a compost bin to reuse all of your food scraps and yard clippings.

16. Bring your own reusable cloth bags when shopping, or reuse previous grocery bags.

17. Buy vintage clothing from resale shops and donate old clothes and shoes to groups that can reuse them. Tons of clothing items end up in landfills every year, by reusing clothing we are reducing the landfill size.

18. Use rechargeable batteries and take batteries, as well as other biohazards, to the appropriate facility for disposal.

19. Buy appliances and goods with the Energy Star label, an indication of better environmental performance.

20. Join a group in your community to help educate the public to conserve and go green by reducing, reusing and recycling.

Your efforts can make a huge impact on the environment. Remember, think global and act local for ongoing success in greening and living in a healthier environment.

Chapter Eight

Naked Action—Examples From Real Life

∞

Remember when I spoke to you of how caring for others and the environment encourages positive feelings? Caring for the earth and greening your surroundings by practicing my conservation plan will contribute to these positive feelings and better mental health attitude. Combine that with being outdoors in nature, regular exercise, and good nutrition. You are creating an environment where you can feel less depressed and more energized.

Being green means being more mindful of your actions, being healthier in all ways requires mindfulness as well. Many in the world have become aware of the Buddhist technique of Mindfulness-Based Stress Reduction (MBSR). Jon Kabat-Zinn originally suggested this technique utilizing MBSR training as a way to relieve stress, particularly for people with chronic pain and stress-related disorders.

Mindfulness is at the heart of the MBSR Buddhist training as it promotes being very still and aware of the present. The MBSR technique says not to dwell on the past or on the future, but to bring your attention to the precise present activity you are participating in. According to this concept, most people float through life spending much of their time lost in the pain and confusion of past issues. They, therefore, miss the present day activities. They "check out" of experiencing the present because of the stress that is inherently there when they do not focus on the "now." A by-product of this effect is that life often seems to lack meaning and strength for the participant.

Mindfulness is more than just being aware of what we are currently focused on and doing; it is also being aware of what we are thinking and feeling. Mindfulness allows you to be aware of when you have negative thoughts. It is easy to spend untold hours, days, or even weeks criticizing yourself or justifying and blaming yourself or others. Yet you would never think of making a conscious decision to spend all that time enveloped in self-criticism or blame. You would never think of self-inflicting stress. It might seem like your thoughts or feelings are out of control, but by being mindful you can refocus those negative energies we all have and find purpose.

Please be clear that I am not suggesting everyone should be a Buddhist, this is not the point. Instead, I am suggesting that you should be more mindful of your actions, particularly in relationship in caring for yourself and others. By being mindful of what you are doing in the present, you are focusing your brain on positive behaviors. Your choices become healthier when you think them through. It is not always easy to be mindful. It is a skill which requires practice. It is also a skill well worth developing and can be applied to most everything in one's life.

By experiencing nature regularly, as well as caring for the earth and its denizens, you are making a mindful choice to refocus your lifestyle and do something positive with it. Practicing the Green and Simple Conservation Plan means you ARE doing something constructive for the world and for yourself. You are moving in a direction which is healthier for all involved and making yourself feel better while doing it.

Al Gore encourages the community through the book, *An Inconvenient Truth*, to reduce, reuse and recycle in efforts to improve global warming. In fact, Nobel laureate and former Vice President Gore has begun a special campaign to get more grass roots interest in solving the global warming crisis; it is called the We Campaign and is a non-profit, non-partisan effort to improve the world's environmental situation. The suggestions offered by the We Campaign begin educating people how buying less wasteful products and reusing things we already have in the community can be just the beginning of more mindful practices related to the environment. Take your concern a step further—carbon dioxide is not the only gas or chemical that is causing our earth illness. Due to exposure to chemicals, there are many in our world who suffer from illness and injury. The sad truth is many private and public entities are choosing to ignore the warning signs, much as are ignoring global warming. This means it is our responsibility as individuals to make our homes and communities safe. You know what is right. You want to protect your family and this earth. You want to feel better every day—greening and conservation will help make that happen.

Now is the time to get started and this is your opportunity to make the world a better place. Get started with the Green and Simple Conservation Plan today!

Mr. Answerman and the Incredible Recycling Dog

Recently, I had the distinct privilege of meeting Luna, the Incredible Recycling Dog. Her owner, Jim Kleinwachter, testifies to Luna's amazing ability and invited me over one morning to show me how wonderful she truly is. When I came over to meet Luna, an English Springer Spaniel, Kleinwachter told me his strong belief that animals can improve a person's health. Luna and he often go hunting together and share time walking and exercising outdoors. Kleinwachter feels Luna has encouraged him to be healthier. After seeing Luna's exuberant enthusiasm for walking, running, and recycling, I agree.

Luna adores her master and excitedly runs in front of him wherever he walks. If he changes direction, she does too, anxiously jumping in front of him to protect him on his travels. We walked his expansive nature-filled backyard with Luna happily wagging and turning to check that we were safe every few minutes. The grounds are beautiful, yet Kleinwachter uses no fertilizers or excessive chemical weed killers on the property to help keep Luna and the other native plants and animals which live there safe.

There is something else that makes Luna particularly special. Luna is "off color" according to her breeder. Springer Spaniels are supposed to have dark patches over the eyes and ears with a white stripe down the nose: if they do not, they cannot be shown at dog shows. Many breeders put these mis-colored dogs down, killing them for no other reason than they have poor coloring. Luna was lucky—the Kleinwachter family found her before that happened. Kleinwachter and his family are eternally grateful for the love of their dog Luna and feel she has contributed to the family's health and emotional connection with nature. Kleinwachter grins and says, "One man's trash is another man's treasure!"

Kleinwachter stopped, plopped down a recycling bin and said, "Now watch this!" In astonishment, I watch as Luna repeatedly picks up plastic bottles and deposits them in the recycle

Luna, the Incredible Recycling Dog, recycling a can with her owner and best friend, Jim Kleinwachter.

bin. She excitedly runs in circles wagging her tail and waiting for more recycling duty. She repeated it dozens of times and Kleinwachter said she would do it all day if he let her. Luna IS the Incredible Recycling Dog!

Jim Kleinwachter is a conservationist, and is as unique and special as his dog Luna. He is tall, at 6'4", and I have found many people look up to him, not because of his height, but because he has dedicated his life to educating people about conservation and making a difference in his community. While Luna helps him with the basics, Kleinwachter has truly expanded on this and become a special part of his local community.

Kleinwachter has become a mentor for me in relationship to environmental education. I met Kleinwachter over nine years ago. I remember the exact day. He managed his family owned hardware store in the local community. Little did I know then how my life would be changed because of his influence and on-going mentoring of my conservation and environmental knowledge.

That particular summer day I was going to the hardware store to consider paint. My husband and I had recently been married and I had moved into Kleinwachter's small community. Standing in front of the large paint display, I frowned and thought about color. Kleinwachter asked if I wanted help and I told him I could not afford any of his paint. "No problem! There's a paint recycling center nearby. Maybe you can find some free paint there." Paint recycling. The beginning of my conservation education—I had never thought of it before.

Over that first year in my new community I often went into Kleinwachter's hardware store. He was the answer guru—always teaching, guiding and mentoring me in ways to improve my household. Almost all of his suggestions were the most economical and were distinctly conservation minded. The hardware store was sold and I did not hear from him for many years.

Conservation @ Home sign which property owners display proudly.

Then one day a few years ago I joined a community organization and met Kleinwachter again. I squinted at him from across the room. Suddenly it dawned on me, "Hey! I know where I know you from!" He raised his eyebrows. "You're the hardware manager who always helped me!" That was the beginning of a great friendship with a man I have come to know as "Mr. Answerman"—my personal environmental encyclopedia.

Kleinwachter's knowledge of ecological and conservation issues comes from a life-long concern for nature and the environment. It makes sense that he taught his best bud, Luna, how to recycle! Kleinwachter is a Land Protection Specialist and works tirelessly through The Conservation Foundation in Illinois to educate individual homeowners on how they can make a difference by practicing conservation. Kleinwachter has created and heads a division of The Conservation

Jim Kleinwachter and volunteers cleaning up the river with the DuPage River Sweep Program.

Foundation called Conservation @ Home which has pulled over 400 residents from Illinois to practice better home conservation. He co-founded and coordinated the DuPage River Sweep Program, which has extended into three counties in Illinois and has been responsible for removing over fifty tons of debris from local rivers. His dream has been to bring the scientifically based and sometimes complicated environmental issues and translate them so the average homeowner can understand and participate in conservation more easily.

The remarkable thing about Kleinwachter is that no matter the question I throw at him, and believe me, I have thrown hundreds of environmental questions at the poor man, he always knows the answer. Soon our emails jokingly shared subject lines with the title, "Mr. Answerman To The Rescue." He has certainly become my personal mentor in the conservation world and has helped me learn more than I ever imagined. This is also what I recommend for you. If you feel daunted by the overwhelming issues related to greening and conservation, one of the best things to do is find a friend who can be a mentor and help guide you with home conservation much as Kleinwachter has helped guide me. Even if your friend knows very little about greening and conservation, perhaps you can learn more together. This book is a start of course, but caring for your property and the environment is an on-going process. Finding a friend who can help you learn more to expand your conservation plan will help you both, and remember the ultimate benefit will be that you will get healthier when exposed to less chemicals and practice better environmental care.

Kleinwachter, of course, has devoted his life to this. Recently, I asked him why he is so tirelessly dedicated to conservation. His reply, "My philosophy is that we all have a responsibility to leave this planet in better shape than we found it. Typically, people think government will take care of these things—everything will be fine—and they need not contribute. They say, 'What will my efforts matter?' I try to change that attitude: it DOES matter!"

He is able to educate people through The Conservation Foundation. To begin with, he has developed a long list of conservation Fact Sheets which he has made available on the Conservation @ Home website. The fact sheet link is located at the back of this book. More importantly, he has developed a way for interested homeowners to be linked with friends in conservation by participating in the Conservation @ Home Program. Some of the goals of the program include encouraging water conservation by promoting native landscaping, encouraging the "think global, act local" mindset in communities, rewarding landowners for using good conservation practices, educating landowners on how to create wildlife habitat's in their own gardens, and creating a group of united homeowners who can get to know one another and build a conservation community. Each homeowner receives a Conservation @ Home sign which they proudly display on their property when they have achieved a Conservation @ Home status.

Another benefit of educating the public for Kleinwachter and his lovely dog, Luna, is they have made friends in the community. Working with the public, learning more about and helping care for the people and nature within his community has contributed to Kleinwachter's overall health. He looks good, feels good, and is living a satisfied lifestyle. I asked him about why he participates in all the organizations he does which help the community. Kleinwachter said, "It makes me feel good to get out and make a difference. I meet people and get to know them; I help them. It's an exhilarating feeling to know that I have a purpose in life and that purpose is to help others live a better and healthier lifestyle."

How You Can Practice Conservation @ Home

Kleinwachter's Conservation @ Home team encourages and recognizes property owners that protect and/or create yards that are environmentally friendly and conserve water. This includes planting native vegetation, such as prairie and woodland wildflowers, trees and shrubs, creating butterfly and rain gardens, and removing invasive species of plants. Loss of open space and wildlife habitat and dirty rainwater run-off are the leading causes of environmental degradation in our developed areas. If you can replace some of this lost habitat in your yard, then you can help reduce some of the negative impacts of development in your community.

Yards with native landscaping reduce local flooding and clean pollution from rainwater run-off before it reaches our rivers, lakes and ponds. Native planting can be incorporated into any landscape style and provides a healthier backyard environment for your family to enjoy.

Whether it is creating a butterfly or rain garden using native landscaping, utilizing organic fertilizers, or removing invasive plants from your property, every little thing you do on your property makes a difference in cleaning up our water, providing natural habitat, and creating healthy landscapes for people and wildlife.

Below is a guide from Conservation @ Home which educates you on how to build a butterfly garden.

HOW TO BUILD A
NATIVE BUTTERFLY GARDEN

There are many species of butterflies common to the United States. Attracting them to your yard is easily done with a butterfly garden—or a flower garden planted with native nectar-rich plants that attract butterflies. Butterfly gardens can be large or small and can be adapted to almost any soil conditions. Plant a butterfly garden now and watch the beautiful winged critters appear!

Swallowtail butterfly on Allium flower in Shawna's 2007 garden.

- Butterfly gardens are easy to construct, require little water once established and no fertilizers.

- Plant perennials, which establish themselves and bloom each year. This makes a beautiful butterfly garden for years to come!

- Plants that attract butterflies should be planted in full sun, and ideally in a place where the wind is blocked (butterflies do not like to fight the wind).

- With the great variety of native plants available, you can plan your garden to have colorful blooms from early spring to late fall.

- If you prefer smaller plantings, a few butterfly-attracting plants can be placed within your existing garden.

- No chemical fertilizers or pesticides should be used, as butterflies and other wildlife are extremely sensitive to them and the native plants do not need them.

- Native plants that produce bright pink, orange, yellow and red colors attract butterflies.

- Native plants are those that were originally found local to your community; therefore they require little maintenance, less water, and less money to support! Most native plants can be found in nurseries which specialize in selling native plants local to your community.

The Legacy of Katherine, Queen of the Tot-Fairies

There is an incredible family I have met that has inspired me in many ways. Jean-Marie Kauth, PhD. is an Assistant Professor at a university and her husband, Craig W. Colling, PhD., works as a chemical engineer. For over seventeen years Jean-Marie and Craig have worked tirelessly to provide a chemical-free and environmentally-friendly home for themselves and for their children. Perhaps because of their work history, they are both uniquely clued-in to provide an eco-friendly place for their family to live and play in comfort.

They practice a vigorous schedule of greening with words like "reduce, reuse, and recycle" being common discussion within their family. Jean-Marie and Craig work to use less chemicals within their household and on their lawn, leave windows open in the summer to conserve energy instead of using air-conditioning, and use less natural resources wherever they can.

Meeting them has been an inspiration. They practice far better conservation techniques than I do—I have learned from them. They have also endured an overwhelming environmental tragedy. More than any other message in this book I hope their message gets through to you so a similar tragedy will not happen to your family.

The community they lived in practiced night-time pesticide spraying, but Jean-Marie and Craig were unaware of this. They were never notified of the spraying. Soon after the regular spraying of the pesticides occurred, Jean-Marie and Craig began to see their entire family, but most specifically, their daughter, Katherine, become seriously ill.

In 1997 the couple's son and daughter went through unexplained severe asthma episodes. This led to long-term breathing treatments at a local clinic. Katherine began exhibiting other symptoms such as fatigue and fevers. In July of that year Katherine was diagnosed with Leukemia. The family immediately began treatment for Katherine's cancer, and she did well until the next summer.

The summer of 1999 was traumatic for Katherine as she had another relapse. The doctors were enormously surprised as she had been doing so well. Jean-Marie and Craig began to wonder why Katherine was severely ill only during the summer. She was desperately sick that summer and nearly died from several infections that attacked her weakened system. Katherine suffered terribly, but still, she survived.

In November of that year she had to have a bone marrow transplant. This was followed by intense chemotherapy and radiation; she lost every hair on her body and had to be on morphine for the pain from the radiation damage in her esophagus. There was more illness, so much more. The family had to split up while Katherine lived at the Ronald McDonald House in Milwaukee for four months during treatment. They watched the other children and their friends in the house die from the illnesses they were being treated for. It was tragic and difficult for Katherine, yet still she lived. Her strength of will surpassed anything the family could imagine.

Then in August of 2000 Craig and Jean-Marie were lying in bed at their home trying to think of ways to protect Katherine further. They had installed a reverse osmosis water filter and a HEPA air filter and were trying to eat mostly organic vegetables to avoid chemical residues. Jean-Marie said, "We kept our windows open at night to get the good quality air circulated. At about 11:00 PM we heard a strange buzzing noise outside our window. We had heard the sound occasionally before, but had always though the city was sweeping the streets. However, a few days before we had heard rumors that they sprayed the forest preserve with a pesticide and we put two and two together." With the sudden realization that toxic pesticides might be making their family ill, they leapt into a panic.

Jean Marie Kauth, and her daughter, Katherine.

Calling the police, the couple found out the city was spraying pesticides to kill mosquitoes. Jean-Marie burst into tears and begged them to stop the spraying. Police arrived at her house shortly thereafter, and the couple went out to greet the officer and could smell the odor of what were the pesticides. The officer tracked down the truck and brought back a flyer After investigation, it turned out that the company was using Dursban, a dangerous chemical known to be particularly toxic to children. Jean-Marie's hope for her daughter faltered. She said about the incident, "I was certain that this was it; Katherine's hard-earned last chance was gone."

Craig and Jean-Marie began a full-out plea to the city to stop the spraying. They felt strongly that the city had violated their property with the pesticides, effectively spraying full-strength carcinogenic chemicals into their windows without informing them of the effects. Both Craig and Jean-Marie spent hours and hours researching and bringing detailed toxicology information to the city, the state, and the Environmental Protection Agency. The chemical company refused to speak with the couple, saying it was in their right to sell the product for the use dictated.

It was Katherine's desire to live a full life where she did not have to suffer and neither would any other children. Little Katherine, after suffering more pain and trauma than most adults can imagine, helped form a plan with her parents to get the word out on pesticide spraying. Katherine knew that one person could make a difference. With her family, she mobilized her family and community to distribute "stop pesticide spraying" flyers all around her city. Her insightful quote about government decision makers who decide to continue to spray toxic chemicals even when they know it can hurt people: "But don't they love their children?"

Katherine, in an amazing testimony to the power of her belief that one person can make a difference, walked door-to-door with her family and friends to distribute the flyers even though she was quite ill. It was time well-spent because that November, there was a ballot initiative for the city, and 75% of the voting citizens opposed supporting on-going mosquito spraying. It was a small and sad victory for Katherine's family, but an enormous victory for the other children in the community who might have become ill because of the spraying. One person can make a difference. Katherine made a difference for all those other people who might have been exposed to a carcinogenic environmental hazard.

Katherine's suffering because of her cancer was extensive, and sadly, soon became worse. Chemotherapy had to be used to kill the leukemia cells. Her parents watched as she screamed in pain because the chemotherapy had destroyed her intestines; she lost all her hair and eyelashes, her belly was swollen and she had wasted away. She spent her seventh year secluded in a room at the hospital lonely and in pain. Finally, after she recovered from the last round of chemotherapy in 2001, Katherine was able to experience a semi-normal life and second grade at a real school. It was her dream come true. She made friends and laughed again; Katherine was finally able to touch and live life.

Jean-Marie built a fairy garden for Katherine so she would be able to experience nature more closely. Katherine dictated several books to her mother, all based on "Katherine, Queen of the Tot-Fairies." Her mother is currently illustrating them in hopes of publishing them to inspire others. They are stories of a little girl's love of nature and her hope that all children can be free of pain and illness and experience nature and the world more closely.

Katherine's desire was the same as her parents: that the place we live in be safe for everyone. Living in a toxic environment is something many do without ever realizing it. Local governments, corporations, and private citizens spray chemicals without understanding the deadly effects. Chemicals can be invisible and odorless, but very deadly to insects, animals, fish and humans. There are many chemicals humans are exposed to which are known to cause various forms of cancer. When I researched the names of some of these chemicals and learned more about them to see how Jean-Marie and Craig's family might have been poisoned, I was down-right shocked. If you do not know what types of chemicals are publicly used in your community, it is time for you to contact your local government and find out.

The National Cancer Institute says that Benzene, Propur, Cypermethrin, Chlorpyrifos, Malathion, DDT, and hundreds of other carcinogens produce adverse effects in the human body and lead to cancerous developments. Toxicologists nationwide have been screaming their concern for years over community exposures to airborne agricultural pesticides and other chemicals. Yet, most of them are still in use in various places across the country.

The chemical companies argue their chemicals do not cause Leukemia or any other illness; government studies disagree. However, the government often does not hold the answers regarding the chemicals due to laws and regulations that allow the chemicals to continue in use. Regulation and testing is sometimes left up to individual firms, which can leave many people feeling confused. In the end, there are more and more cancer pockets developing across the country, areas where there is a heavy concentration of cancer patients suffering from similar mysterious illnesses due to toxic exposure.

Chemical exposure and contamination is one of the single largest issues in relationship to conservation. There are many ways to get exposed to these chemicals, such as landfill leaks and contamination, insecticide spraying, food spraying, household cleaning and much, much more. If you do only one thing in relation to the Green and Simple Conservation Plan, please avoid using chemical solutions on your property as much as you can. Encourage your community to utilize safe practices with chemicals as well so your environment is as clean as it can be.

On June 22, 2002, Katherine, Queen of the Tot-Fairies, beautiful champion for young children every where, died a horrible, painful death. Jean-Marie suffered with her. She said Katherine's last few weeks were the worst, "Katherine would often wake and say, "Mommy, I survived the night!' after recording messages to loved ones when she thought she would not [survive another night]." Saddened, frightened, delirious, and tortured by her illness, an illness fostered by chemical exposure, she begged her mother to come with her and not let her be alone in death. Her last intelligible words were, "Everyone loses everyone."

Her parents and siblings are now singing Katherine's swan song: they have dedicated their lives to spreading the message of utilizing safe chemicals for the environment. Both Craig and Jean-Marie work diligently to encourage safe lawn and garden treatments. Katherine's dream was that all children would be safe. That means utilization of safe lawn chemicals, safe mosquito control choices, safe house-hold cleaning products and much more.

Katherine's family feels that she should never have died, but now that she has, her short life and incredible inspiration should not be wasted. Her heartbreaking life, as tragic and painful as it was, has brought light onto a dark and difficult subject. Katherine believed she could make a difference, and even in death, she is still touching the world with her gentle hope.

Once upon a time there was an amazing little girl who imagined a world where there were no harmful chemicals to hurt children. She dreamed of a natural and safe world where food, air, and land have not been poisoned. Her name was Katherine. Her legacy, the brilliant white-hot result of her short life, is to inspire the world to practice better conservation so that all children can live in safety and health.

Beautiful Katherine, Queen of the Tot-Fairies.

Conservation In The Community—SCARCE Is Making A Difference!

Necessity is the mother of invention. In the case of School and Community Assistance for Recycling & Composting Education, a not-for-profit environmentally-centered community outreach program in DuPage County, Illinois, necessity was the spark that made it possible for Greg and Kay McKeen to forever change the global community for the better.

In 1988, Kay McKeen joined a large team of concerned friends and family to build a new recycling center in Wheaton, Illinois. After the recycling center was complete, the team that built it realized the need for education. McKeen was particularly disturbed that the local community seemed unconcerned about recycling. McKeen and her team understood it was not a lack of concern for the environment and intensifying landfill requirements; it was a lack of knowledge about environmental issues.

McKeen understood that educating the public would be the first step to stimulate positive environmental change. She decided, with her family's support, to form an organization to help educate the community on greening the Earth. With major funding support from the DuPage County Board, McKeen and her team of do-gooders built SCARCE. McKeen now manages the organization and it has become the go-to resource in the community for environmentally friendly education.

Little did McKeen know that what started as a small not-for-profit facility to educate the local community, would grow into an organization which would touch thousands of people worldwide. SCARCE's success puts a new spin on the popular phrase, "Think global; act local."

SCARCE has multiple programs to help both the local and international community and is currently housed in a 5,100-square-foot facility with a warehouse, two libraries, and many workshop and project rooms. Hundreds of volunteers come together to assist SCARCE and make a difference for the global community. McKeen gets college interns from schools such as Stanford, University of Iowa, Elmhurst College, and more.

When teachers began telling McKeen that books were being

Kay McKeen, Manager of the not-for-profit organization, SCARCE, sorting used books at the SCARCE warehouse facility.

SCARCE intern John Mulrow (far right), Stanford Class of 2009, educating local high school students, Ian Vitalis and Zach Kocanda, through a program John developed as part of his internship called "Sustainability and You."

thrown into landfills, SCARCE stepped in with a special book rescue program to give them to children in need. Currently, the SCARCE library hosts over 25,000 books at a time. Local schools and organizations with disadvantaged or low-income students are welcome to choose books free of charge. Teachers are able to access an online inventory to make selections.

The book rescue program has also made a large global impact. Hundreds of children around the world have received books in schools, orphanages, hospitals, confined youth centers, and libraries, because from SCARCE. Books have been sent to communities in Kenya, China, India, Lithuania, Mexico, Columbia, Honduras, Costa Rica, Uganda, South Africa, Russia, Cambodia, and many more. The global impact is staggering as approximately 25 percent of the countries in the world have been touched by the loving hand of SCARCE.

McKeen and her team have rescued more than three million books from the landfill and helped educate hundreds of thousands of individuals worldwide. The book rescue, like most of the SCARCE operations, is supported entirely by donations and is staffed by volunteers. In bringing the community together to support the book rescue program, McKeen began to see how community and caring for the environment work together.

When McKeen sees an opportunity to rescue something from the landfill, she simply does it. She wants everyone to have that mentality. As an example, when McKeen began picking up used books, she found furniture and old pianos which were about to be tossed into the garbage. Shocked that these items were being thrown away, she began rescuing them. Her team has rescued more than fifteen pianos for needy schools and tons of furniture for educational facilities.

Tools 4 Schools was one of the first programs SCARCE instituted through a

Tools 4 Schools volunteer, Matt Gallup, sorting school supply donations.

special grant provided by the Tellabs Foundation. McKeen says, "Every year thousands of usable school products and office supplies, such as crayons, paper, markers, and books, are thrown into landfills. The enormous negative impact this has on the environment is devastating. We formed Tools 4 Schools to help the local community turn the negative into a positive."

Through teachers workshops and other educational programs, McKeen and her staff were able to bring dozens of elementary and high schools into the program. The office and school products are dropped off at the SCARCE facility, sorted, and redistributed to hundred of area teachers who need them to assist in educating children.

Super Crayons became a spin-off from the Tools 4 Schools program. Used or broken crayons are donated to SCARCE, and then melted down to make "super crayons." The crayons are peeled, sorted, melted in a crock pot, and poured into candle molds to form large crayons which are used by disabled children who have grasping disabilities. Tens of thousands of Super Crayons have been made by individual volunteers as well as local high school environmental clubs. Super Crayons are distributed worldwide and have really made a difference in the lives of physically challenged children.

McKeen commented, "Crayons are petroleum based products. Seeing this precious resource left in a landfill when there are children in need just doesn't make sense. I was inspired by the teachers of handicapped, visually impaired, and autistic children who needed a creative solution to assist these children to grasp crayons. When I was a student, I enjoyed candle making—I applied this concept to melting and reforming used crayons. We send the Super Crayons all over the country, and are now sending the crayons internationally for victims of land mines who have had their fingers blown off."

Before long it became obvious that most anything could be recycled if processed properly. McKeen saw the need to expand the recycling program beyond educational institutions. SCARCE began recycling cell phones, ink cartridges, and plastic bottles. The twenty-ounce bottle reuse program allows the bottles to be reused as product containers instead of going through the energy consuming process of melting down to recycle the bottles.

Another example of this opportunistic thinking is the gym shoe rescue, a program in existence for more than ten years. McKeen works with the Nike Grind Program whereby gym shoes are ground up and reused to make playgrounds and other cool products to help children. She noticed that some shoes, which would not be accepted by Nike Grind, were still in good condition, so she and her team started donating them to needy and homeless individuals in the United States and internationally. In 2008 SCARCE recycled an amazing 18,000 pairs of shoes.

Partnering with church and not-for-profit organizations has expanded this program significantly. SCARCE distributed over 9,000 pairs of shoes in 2008 for reuse through several partner programs. Shoes went to an orphanage in Haiti, veterans in the United States, and homeless and disadvantaged individuals through Wayside Cross Church. They also sent shoes to New Orleans hurricane victims, Share Your Souls, labor programs, and many other groups who collect shoes for reuse. In 2008, an exciting addition to the program happened when a shoe manufacturing company contacted SCARCE about an overrun of hundreds of left shoes. McKeen's team contacted the Range Of Motion Project, an international organization that provides prosthetic limbs and orthotic braces to those who cannot afford or do not have access to these services, and sent the left shoes to this needy organization.

McKeen volunteers tirelessly. She spends hundreds of hours annually meeting with and educating city governments, church facilities, educational institutions of all levels, corporations, and individuals on environmental concerns. One of her goals has been to educate others on how they can build SCARCE-like facilities in other communities. To this end, she and her team have assisted in starting up several groups in the Midwest. She has also taught dozens of local communities how to create and manage "Recycling Extravaganzas." These events are when organizations come together to collect large quantities of recyclables. Recently, one community Recycling Extravaganza collected over nine tons of scrap metal, twelve tons of damaged books and cardboard for recycling, fifty-three tons of electronic recyclables, 450 cell phones, 354 eyeglasses, 306 American flags, 332 bicycles, 340 gym shoes, and 228 car and boat batteries. The list continues on to include paper, keys, clothing, and much more. This was the result of a one-day rescue drive. Imagine how many recyclables have been rescued from the landfills in the dozens of Extravaganzas SCARCE has managed.

SCARCE is changing the lives of many by educating low-income families on creative ways to recycle products of all kinds to better support themselves. The organization also teaches people how to recycle "trash" and "junk" into useful items, such as stationery products and household tools, through

Volunteers at the library warehouse room at SCARCE headquarters in DuPage County, Illinois. From left to right, Whitney Gould, intern from Augustana, Brittney Graham, intern form University of Iowa, Cory Coffman, intern from Carroll University, Linda Knapp, SCARCE educator, Janet LeWald, SCARCE newsletter editor, and Kay McKeen.

their Trash To Treasure program. McKeen feels it is everyone's responsibility to help the community learn how to think outside the box to be greener and healthier in their lifestyles. It is the right thing to do.

All of the programs run by this unique organization tie into the need for education on greening and environmental issues. SCARCE is always in desperate need of volunteers and financial supporters so it can expand its programs to touch even more lives. McKeen sees a future where everyone does his or her part to help the community be greener and more environmentally friendly. "What I have learned is that recycling involves more than an industrial meltdown process. It involves people who care about each other and their community. Giving back to the world can happen on a large scale—globally—when you start to think with a 'greener' attitude locally. You can make a difference for your community. You can make a difference for the citizens of Earth. All it takes is a little effort!"

Get out in your community and make a difference like Kay McKeen has—help the world take back its natural resources and go green by reducing, reusing, and recycling everything you can.

Part III— Building a Green Community Plan

"Never doubt that a small group of thoughtful citizens can change the world.
Indeed, it is the only thing that ever has."

—MARGARET MEAD

A	K	E	#	A	#	F	R
M	:	L	4	S	!	%	I
#	L	O	6	M	X	Y	E
D	I	N	?	I	M	Z	N
N	V	G	A	L	O	2	D
A	E	E	N	E	R	1	#
#	!	R	D	%	E	?	#
Y	P	P	A	H	#	E	B

Chapter Nine

Building a Green Community Plan

∞

F eeling better is closely connected to our brain function. Relationship building and healing—building close emotional connections within society—according to Richard O'Connor, Ph.D., is one of the ways we can feel better because we are stimulating regrowth of brain cells. This helps our brain better transmit chemicals. If serotonin, as an example, is in ample supply and is moving as it should within our system, we are far more likely to feel better about ourselves and our surroundings.

Obviously, improving one's physical health is important to keeping brain function strong. A healthy body should equal a healthy brain, right? But I think building relationships, much as O'Connor suggests, is an important way to bring us more closely in touch and make us feel better through better brain function. Being closer to community means we are seeing, touching, and communicating with other human beings. Community, particularly a green community, starts at home with family.

Building a good foundation is important to any endeavor. The foundation in your community is your family. Building family community means bringing your family together. It is taking those eight-year-olds away from their TV-filled bedrooms and pulling them into conversations regularly. It is making amends with your siblings over childhood issues that are in the past and deserve to be left there. It is caring for your parents, accepting them for who they are, and inviting them to your home often no matter how far away they live. It is telephoning your elderly relatives once in a while and sharing your life with them. These examples are the beginning, but it is all of these things and more.

According to William J. Diehm, "In 1987, 8.5 million elderly lived alone; by 2020, 13.3 million elderly will live alone." He goes on to say, "Loneliness is often caused by wanting people to do something for us. When we do things for other people, we are never lonely. Self-referenced thinking often leads to a barrenness of spirit that breeds discontent and loneliness."

Elderly family members are usually isolated and need someone to unite them with others. Keeping up family connections helps the elderly live longer, as well as keeping their faculties and brain functions longer, so they can enjoy life far into their elder years.

Uniting your family community can improve everyone's outlook. Children are dependent on adults to educate them on the process of building community. Often, children learn more and grow up with better mental health when they have a wider range of family members to support and educate them in this process. Each one of us can make a difference for our family community by helping prevent isolationism.

Once we have built family community, it is important to expand your view and build community outside the home. Building neighborhood community is important for your own personal emotional growth and for the greater community in which you live. One of the most important items on the *Get Your Green On Health Philosophy* list is volunteering—working with others in the community. I believe that helping others is a special way to strengthen the emotional health which helps you foster a positive mental attitude.

The bottom line is that bringing people together to work on a project can enhance your life significantly. Community building allows you to invest in environmental health and beauty by improving your neighborhood, building relationships, and evangelizing all levels of health and caring interaction. It also improves your health by getting you off that couch and out into the community where you can share and build unique

Shawna and Harry the Pug having fun at home in the garden. Photo by Kelsey Connors.

friendships which can last a lifetime. It is good for everyone.

Remember back at the beginning of the book when I told you about my conversation with Stacey? That conversation touched on a known fact that pets help reduce loneliness. Stroking, touching, and loving our pets is a great way to feel better. Pets are a part of our community and are particularly for someone who is living alone. They comfort.

Taking care of a pet is an important contribution to a family and even a neighborhood community. My neighborhood block parties would not be complete without all of our pets out visiting and being a part of the fray. Our household has both a dog and a cat within it. Harry the Pug has become my constant companion both inside and outside the home. Caring for pets makes most people's lives feel warmer and richer.

Along those lines, building a strong green community is important in a similar way. In that same conversation with Stacey, I touched on the need to care for the world. By building, growing, and tending plants in the garden as well as caring for the larger natural environment, your mood and outlook are elevated. It happens much the same way as it does when touching a pet; by touching, digging, and building in the soil you feel better. For me, being out in nature and, most specifically, gardening, puts me in a meditative state. The way I feel is energized and upbeat. According to my doctors, it is a combination of things that brings me to a meditative state while gardening; sunlight exposure, repetitive tasks, and steady breathing are part of it. It is also the people I meet and the social aspect of gardening. I do not realize I am in a meditative state at the time; I simply feel good. Meditation improves serotonin production. It also lowers heart rate, blood pressure, and stress levels. Among other things, it is supposed to reduce anxiety, help with chronic pain, diseases, and much, much more. Gardening is doing all of that for me. Feeling this is something I want you to experience as well.

This is just one of the reasons why, when I consider building community, I prefer to join environmental organizations. Then I combine my outdoor health plan with groups that are already centered on outdoor activities. I feel good knowing my hands are in the soil a lot, and I am encouraging others to do this as well. Teaching people how to be green and live a life which encourages healthy home conservation practices and discourages wasteful activities seems like the right thing to do. It brings me closer to people and closer to the earth.

There is another reason to build relationships with fellow members of your community. If you can work together to purposely build a green community with attractive landscaping, you can reduce crime!

Everyone wants to improve home value and rid their neighborhood of crime. Building a greener community just might do that. Research findings by Frances E. Kuo, Ph.D., and William C. Sullivan, Ph.D., and their team at the University of Illinois Urbana-Champaign Department of Natural Resources and Environmental Science suggest that by improving green areas in your community you can significantly reduce crime. Their study, titled *Environment and Crime In The Inner City, Does Vegetation Reduce Crime?* Is one of the most significant and ground breaking crime reduction studies of our time.

Here, local boyscouts and members of the community come out to clean up an elementary school bird and butterfly sanctuary.

A quote from the study says, "Although vegetation has been positively linked to fear of crime and crime in a number of settings, recent findings in urban residential areas have hinted at a possible negative relationship: residents living in "greener" surroundings report lower levels of fear, fewer incivilities, and less aggressive and violent behavior. This study used police crime reports to examine the relationship between vegetation and crime in an inner-city neighborhood.

View of a public garden Shawna designed to help public awareness of the economic advantages of community beautification.

Crime rates for 98 apartment buildings with varying levels of nearby vegetation were compared. Results indicate that although residents were randomly assigned to different levels of nearby vegetation, the greener a building's surroundings were, the fewer crimes reported. Furthermore, this pattern held for both property crimes and violent crimes. The relationship of vegetation to crime held after the number of apartments per building, building height, vacancy rate, and number of occupied units per building were accounted for."

This study is an example that proves a community can come together to make a difference. It offers hope to community builders around the world who want to improve their health and know their neighbors. Planting trees, gardens, and "green" as part of your efforts to become more involved in community will do more than look pretty; it will reduce crime rates. This, in itself, is strong motivation to encourage your neighbors to work with you.

There is also a growing community within the work force that is focusing on improving our corporate environment. Businesses are discovering that being green, building unity, and improving the work environment are working together to unite the work force and increase work production.

Building family community gives you a healthier brain and body. Building a green neighborhood community improves property values and reduces crime. Building a positive work community helps us cope better with stress and perform better. Combine these, and make community a large part of your life. The friendships you build will become your support network and enrich your life for as long as you live.

Chapter Ten

Strip Away the Excuses— How To Make Building the Green Community Plan a Reality

∞

Again, building a family community is the beginning of building a larger green community, and building community is a strong step towards positive mental health. Everything you do is watched carefully by your children, so it is important to set an example for them every day. In psychology, they call the simple act of setting an example for your children "modeling."

As human beings, we are not static. We are evolutionary. Life is imperfect and changes constantly. Therefore, we must understand that modeling also becomes evolutionary. Let us say, for example, when you were younger, you were a smoker. Then you learned that smoking was bad for both your health and your children's health, so you decided to quit. Not only did you quit, but you also spent time with your family to teach them why you quit. By leaving behind poor habits, setting positive examples, and educating your family, you improved the lives of everyone in your family—significantly. This is an example of positive health modeling.

Trying to model a more positive lifestyle and self-image is not only possible, it *must* be done to help our children learn to cope with life. Often stress and isolation patterns meld so tightly into our family's brains that they live precisely as they see you living. If your life is so full of stress that you cannot cope well with your own life, your family will model that stress. Their health is as much of a concern as your own. Will they grow up in front of the TV or computer, isolated from friends and life? Are they depressed or overweight? Do they misbehave and act as if they out of control? Can they handle the stress you all must face? Examine your family closely and see how you can build that community to be closer, both to each other and to nature, so you can live a healthier lifestyle together.

Earlier in this book you read about Stacey's fond memories of nature when she was a child. Just bringing up those memories of being out in nature were uplifting, gave her a mental boost, and made her feel more self-confident. What are your memories of nature and the outdoor environment when you were a child? Most everyone has at least one powerful memory of being outdoors, usually with neighborhood friends, experiencing crazy outdoor adventures and loving every minute of it. These memories are fading from our society. Why? My belief is that too many children today rarely go outside.

Shawna Coronado educating children on the benefits of being outdoors, helping nature, and being healthy. Photo by Kelsey Connors.

This issue has been addressed in several books, including a book written by Richard Louv, *Last Child In The Woods*. He says that our family communities are suffering from something called nature-deficit disorder. He cites multiple reasons why children spend less time outdoors, including the growing addiction to electronic media, the surrender of green spaces to urban-sprawl development, modern parents' inflated fears of natural and human predators, and the lawsuits and vandalism threats that have prompted communities nationwide to forbid public admission to their terrain. Louv links children's alienation from nature to attention-deficit hyperactivity disorder, stress, depression, anxiety, as well as childhood obesity.

Teaching our family how to eat well, exercise well, build communities and generally follow an "all things in moderation" pattern is done by positive modeling. Following the *Get Your Green On Healthy Philosophy* is a good beginning. Unplugging our children and helping them live greener and healthier by leading a life modeled on affirmative health and greening activities will help your children learn positive patterns for their adult lives.

Modeling a healthy lifestyle might start at home, but its influence extends all around you to the larger community. Expanding social ties within your neighborhood and community can happen simply by installing additional greenery and natural landscaping according to an article written by Kuo, Sullivan, Coley, & Brunson, called "Fertile ground for community: Inner-city neighborhood common spaces," *American Journal of Community Psychology*, 1998.

The researchers say in the article, "research suggests that the formation of neighborhood social ties may substantially depend on the informal social contact which occurs in neighborhood common spaces, and that in inner-city neighborhoods where common spaces are often barren no-man's lands, the presence of trees and grass supports common space use and informal social contact among neighbors. We found that for 145 urban public housing residents randomly assigned to 18 architecturally identical buildings, levels of vegetation in common spaces predict both use of common spaces and neighborhood social ties; further, use of common spaces mediated the relationship between vegetation and neighborhood social ties. In addition, vegetation and neighborhood social ties were significantly related to residents' senses of safety and adjustment. These findings suggest that the use and characteristics of common spaces may play a vital role in the natural growth of community, and that improving common spaces may be an especially productive focus for community organizing efforts in inner-city neighborhoods."

Volunteers working to improve their community by installing a bulb garden.

In other words, if you improve the environment of your neighborhood, you improve the relationships within the community. The simple effort of planting a tree together can build and improve your emotional connections and sense of responsibility to your neighbors. The Landscape and Human Health Laboratory website mentions, "When the spaces next to residences are green, they are both more attractive and more comfortable, drawing people to them. Such settings support frequent, friendly interaction among neighbors—the foundation of neighborhood social ties. These ties are the heart of a neighborhood's strength, encouraging neighbors to help and protect each other."

Their study is certainly true. Proof of this is in my own neighborhood. Behind my back fence, just bordering my property line on the city easement area, I have a long garden which touches a public sidewalk and bike path. Every time I walk out behind the fence I have kind neighbors stop to talk to me. Most are walking with family. People bike by when I am out working as well and shout

This picture shows the newly planted eastern portion of Shawna's behind-the-fence public garden the first year of growth.

greetings and encouragement. Sometimes cars squeal to a halt on the road beyond the sidewalk just to say hello and cheer me on. It has been one of the most heart-warming things I have experienced related to my garden. Because of that addictive encouragement, I asked my neighbors, Alex and Kristen Cabral, if I could extend the garden onto their easement property as well. They have an additional behind-the-fence area which is approximately sixty-six feet long by seven feet wide sitting in full sun. They encouragingly said yes. I had no money to support this idea, so called all of my gardening friends and asked if they had plants they would be willing to donate to my new "public" garden.

It was truly an exercise in building community to create this perennial garden. Within two weeks I had enough plants to fill up the entire area and dozens of heart-warming stories for each and every plant I was given. I spent time with my gardening friends meeting their families, getting to know them and learning more about the nature surrounding their homes. They laughed with me, exercised with me, and told me about where the plants came from. Each plant has a history, usually involving a lot of love. All my friends felt pride because they had helped me inspire the public either through their gardening advice, or because I planted one of their plants. My gardening friends are from many different backgrounds; Hispanic, African-American, White, Jewish, Indian, Elderly, Children, Hindu, and Christian. We all came together so that more people walking along that public path can enjoy a little bit of beauty and nature. Our backgrounds did not make a difference; but the love we felt when sharing this little spot in our community made a huge difference.

By the time I had finished building the garden it was late fall and the perennials in my cold northern state looked like frozen, brown sticks. Yet, still, people walked by quite frequently. One day a woman stopped me while I was cleaning up outside. She said that she never walked this way until I built the garden, but now she likes to walk by every day to see the progress and because she thinks it

This photo shows the current view of Shawna's expanded behind-the-fence public garden.

is beautiful. I laughed and said it looked like a bunch of sticks to me. She said, "yes, but I see a future when I see this garden. I see that people still care. I see a safe place to live. You care, and we appreciate it." Then she hugged me and walked on. I was left to stare after this stranger I had never met with tears in my eyes thinking how wonderful and affirming it is to share in this type of community experience.

The exciting part of this particular gardening experience is I have started to see more and more gardens built in the neighborhood. People are interested in beautifying and improving their community in a greener fashion if they see an example first. It makes them feel as if they are not isolated. Creating and maintaining something beautiful in nature is healthy and encourages others to come out and do the same thing. It brings people together and it also improves the economy. Therefore you must model to more than just your family community; if you model "healthy and green" for others in your community, you will make a difference for your neighborhood as well.

There are hundreds of ways to get involved with your community in a green way. Park districts, clubs, churches, educational institutions; the list goes on and on. If you prefer to get involved with an environmental organization which might encourage positive green growth in your community, I would contact your local government first. They will know what organizations are already established.

There are many organizations out there that are set up to do beneficial environmental work for your city and neighborhood. For example, America In Bloom (www.americainbloom.org) or Habitat for Humanity's Seed for the future program (www.habitat.org) are prime examples of exciting ways to get started helping others.

If you can not or do not want to join an organization such as this, perhaps you can build a special organization of your own designed to help your community with its unique needs. I have become involved in many community activities: A team of parents and I get together at the local elementary to help weed, clean up, and redesign gardens on the school property. I have gained friends who have enriched my life and made me feel a part of something special within the organizations I volunteer for. It has rewarded me on a deeply emotional level. There are other organizations I am a part of and all have enhanced my sense of belonging. However, none is stronger than my own family. It is a small community, family, and there are sometimes lots of difficulties that you weather in life together. Family is where you should start, because there is no one else who can take care of and laugh with your loved ones better than you. Make a start and spend more time with them. Have them turn off the media and turn on nature. Get healthier together.

In the end, modeling a positive lifestyle is important both for your familial community and for the greater world which you live in. Get started now; there are so many people and organizations that need your help. I encourage all of you to volunteer to help others and to help yourself feel good every day—build a network of supportive friends and all will benefit!

Chapter Eleven

Naked Action—Examples From Real Life

∞

One of the frustrations of living in our modern culture is that it seems people are never satisfied and always want more. They are not happy with a simple life, because they feel that if they have more—more stuff, more technology, more stress—they will be happy. Yet, it occurred to me several years ago that I knew very few people who could call themselves happy.

Society by and large seems dissatisfied because media and popular culture has enticed us away from the basic pleasures of life. It is within your power to take control of your lifestyle and change this negativity. My mindset is one that I feel I have done that with my own life. You can with yours.

As a result of changing my attitude to be more positive, I have discovered something ground breaking, jaw dropping, and earth shattering: I have discovered happy people. People who are satisfied with life—they *do* exist! There is hope that you and your family can have this feel-good experience, too. Community members who are involved in helping their communities are more satisfied with their lives. Their goals are not focused on wanting more, and more, and more; instead, they put forth efforts to be a part of something larger. They participate in experiences where their hearts are warmed and their souls feel complete. Every person who comes to a volunteer event to help a community organization arrives with a smile. I have seen this happen at every event in which I have participated.

Happy volunteers implementing a clean up and improvement plan.

Yes, these people have their own families, their own hard-luck stories, and their own belief systems. But they arrive, ready to work, with a positive mindset and a unified goal. Everyone laughs and jokes and makes the experience a good one. Beyond building a garden or clearing weeds or selling fund-raising items, they are there because the experience enriches their lives and minds emotionally. It can enrich yours too.

There is evidence that strong community ties can help extend your life span. In the small island community of Okinawa near Japan, there are a large number of centenarians—men and women 100 years old and older—and they are all, as they always have been, included in a tight-knit family and community. I discovered this community through an interesting book called *The Okinawa Program: How the World's*

Ushi Okushima, an Okinawan centenarian. (Photo credit: Okinawa Centenarian Study).

Longest-Lived People Achieve Everlasting Health—And How You Can Too. Ultimately, *The Okinawa Program* addresses the benefits of strong social and family ties as well as a healthy diet, exercise, stress management, and other factors which can help extend life.

To me, extending life is just the beginning. Living longer cannot be the only goal. It is the quality of that life that is important—being able to function as an active member of the community into your ninetieth or even your one hundredth year. These Okinawa centenarians are not singularly wealthy. They do not live with a heavy level of technology or media, they do not desire a thinner body or an inordinate level of beauty. They do not crave more stuff, more stress, or more technology—they are satisfied, truly satisfied with who they are. Their community reinforces this mentality. They feel loved and included. *This* is one of the largest ingredients in the satisfaction formula. Keeping a caring family environment and contributing to the community at large makes people feel satisfied with their lives.

Diet also plays a major role for the health of Okinawans. One of their traditional sayings is "hara hachi bu," or eat until you are only 80% full; wise advice for Western communities who eat until the point of glutony. The authors often remind us, throughout the book, that when young Okinawans pick up Western habits, their rates of obesity, illness, and life expectancy start to match ours as well. The point is that total lifestyle mindfulness is what can extend productive life, not any one factor. Community is an enormously important part of this theory, both for *The Okinawa Program* as well as for the *Get Your Green On Healthy Philosophy*.

The bare behind-the-fence public garden before a large extension in the fall of 2007.

One of the personal contributions to the concept of community I have implemented is a community enjoyment garden mentioned earlier in this book. I have installed this garden behind the fence on my easement property which borders a bike and walking sidewalk. This garden has been a tremendous amount of work, but in building it, I have encouraged people to do the same in the surrounding neighborhoods.

The completed portion of Shawna's garden in the summer of 2008—built for the community to enjoy..

While working in the garden I have talked to dozens of people about the economic values of beautifying and improving their property as well as the health and emotional benefits derived from the physical work in nature. This garden has become a beacon to inspire others to improve and enhance their community because it has inspired some to better their own neighborhood by building a garden. This very small section of earth has brought people together and given me immense joy.

This chapter provides further examples of organizations, businesses, and people who are driven to help the greater community. They are here to give you ideas and to encourage you to either join or begin a community organization that helps others and supports better emotional growth for all participating.

America In Bloom In My Local Community

America In Bloom, in particular, is one of my favorite organizations that enhances and builds communities because it encourages people from all sizes of cities and towns to come together to develop and improve their neighborhoods. I have seen both beautiful and amazing changes in my and other cities who have participated in the program. Cities of all sizes participate—from under 5,000 in population to way larger than 1,000,000 in population—all have amazing results.

The national America In Bloom website says, "participating America in Bloom Towns have experienced positive changes in their communities. The kinds of improvements and their intensity may vary, but often include:

- increased levels of civic pride and community involvement;
- cooperation among residents, organizations, businesses and the municipality;
- everyone working toward a common goal: a better place to live, work, play, and visit;
- visible results;
- valuable information and feedback from judges;
- increased property values;
- increased economic development and a positive impact on the retail industry;
- increased tourism and a positive impact on the hospitality industry;
- decreased vandalism; and
- information and cultural exchanges with neighboring, national, and international communities."

Local America In Bloom members join together to plant a public garden at the Warrenville Community Center building in 2007.

The above examples are true and far, far more. America In Bloom is more than gardening or adding floral pockets and hanging baskets in town. By participating in the America in Bloom program, you open up your city for judging with other cities of similar size. Your city is judged in eight categories; floral displays, environmental awareness, landscaped areas, tidiness, urban forestry, heritage preservation, turf and ground covers, and community involvement. Two judges see at least 80 percent of your city and analyze it in these different areas. But they are required to provide detailed documentation with the contest results to all the community participants, along with a large list of helpful suggestions for improvements.

Since my involvement with America In Bloom, I have become far more aware of the needs of my community and how I connect with the greater world beyond my small neighborhood. Meeting dozens and dozens of people who have cleaned up and beautified their cities has been a special experience for me. At the annual America In Bloom symposium, one person told me, "officially this organization is a contest; but from what I can see, everyone has come out a winner. Every single town this organization has touched has become richer and more beautiful."

This type of improvement increases jobs, property val-

Shawna planting a local community improvement garden with an America In Bloom volunteer team.

ues, economic development and enhances the retail industry. For my town it has increased tourism and seems to have decreased vandalism and crime. It has been my pleasure to meet and work with some wonderful people through the local America In Bloom organization. There are dozens of people in our group, and many have become my close friends. A few have impressed me with their kindness and dedication by giving extraordinary amounts of time to the community. They have really made a difference!

Marvin Miller, Making a Difference For Community

America In Bloom is led on a national level by Marvin Miller, Ph.D, who is currently the president of the America In Bloom organization. I have met him many times and each time I do, I am inspired to go one step farther in helping my community. Miller is on a mission to unite caring people across the nation to promote hometown improvement. Miller, by trade, is an agricultural economist working with Ball Horticultural Company and also serves on several other boards including the Seeley Conference board at Cornell University. Miller believes, as I do, that

Marvin Miller, Ph.D

the promotion of community goes beyond the radius of surface enhancements.

Miller knows that promoting community reduces crime, enhances economy, and most importantly, builds relationships to reduce isolation and depression. Improving the human condition is part of the important reason Miller participates on the America In Bloom executive staff. He is going beyond "talking the talk." He also determinedly works in his personal life to improve the quality of his neighborhood and community from an environmental perspective. He is the president of his condominium association. Miller is also the chairman of the landscape and grounds committee. He speaks publicly to many groups about enhancing the en-

America In Bloom volunteers from the Warrenville, Illinois community coming out to show their pride and make a difference.

vironment and working together to build improved natural areas.

Miller, in leading the America In Bloom organization, has encouraged the goal of making the United States a more beautiful, cleaner, healthier, and safer place to live nationwide. He has touched hundreds of lives in his effort to improve the country. When searching for a way to make a difference in your community, Miller encourages people to start small, but think big—building a team will help you more easily accomplish your goals.

Emily Larson, Gardener-Extraordinaire!

Emily Larson was the person who welcomed me at the first America In bloom meeting I attended and volunteers to improve her community every chance she gets. She strongly believes in the health benefits of spending time in the outdoor environment and recommends gardening as a positive resource to begin your healthful experience. Larson also feels that sharing time and making a difference through volunteer work in the community is not only important, but essential to her health.

Larson's garden represents a lifelong story of love and family unity. Through her love of gardening, she has created a natural paradise in her small backyard. Larson was surprised when she first moved out to the suburbs forty years ago. Her children were so excited to see grass and trees that they wanted to play out in nature everyday. This surprising benefit to the health and welfare of her family has encouraged her to be a lifelong gardener.

When Larson decided to add fish ponds to her backyard, she needed help from her children. She was not interested in small token ponds; these

Emily Larson in her summer perennial garden and Koi Pond.

were to be large ponds with room for goldfish and koi to grow. Completed sixteen years ago, some of the original koi are nor more than a foot long. Water lily's, a bog garden, a waterfall, and a host of gorgeous perennials surround the ponds.

Larson is the city clerk in Warrenville, Illinois. She is continuously involved in helping her neighborhood and the city focus on what is important—the people. She strives tirelessly to make a difference. I know Emily Larson, and I see that she is satisfied with who she is. She enjoys being a part of community events and lives a life which is good for her and for others around her. Larson is a wonderful example of how participating in community can help one's life be healthier and more satisfying.

Roger Quackenbush, Greening The World One Step At A Time

Roger Quackenbush is a man with a unique environmental vision. He and I met while attending an America In Bloom meeting. Quackenbush and his wife, Cynthia, moved into my community about eight years ago. They are now heavily involved and reaping the rewards of close friendships and the sense of belonging that happens when

Roger Quackenbush began improving the environment by starting at home with his family and garden. Here he is with his summer perennial garden.

connecting with others in a community. He credits his son, Christian, with giving him the push to get more involved. He started by coaching soccer at the local Park District and has been the leader of his son's Cub Scout Pack.

Quackenbush soon saw the benefits of building a better world for his son—a place where his son could grow within the community in a healthier way. He wanted to set an example for Christian. Focusing on the environment and community, he began donating thousands of bulbs and plants to the America In Bloom organization in Warrenville, Illinois from the flower and bulb company he runs called Tulips N More. He also sponsors Cub Scout clean-up days to help educate his son on keeping the environment clean and healthy. This small start led to much more. Before long, Quackenbush began to see that he could make a difference by creating positive environmental changes on a much larger scale.

As often happens when one starts volunteering to help the world, the question of how he could make a better future for Christian and the millions of children on earth became more critical. Quackenbush, as an environmental, health, and safety director for a chemical company, has worked regularly on projects which help communities from a chemically-aware standpoint. His vision was to expand on that and find ways to utilize chemical waste bi-products and alternative energy sources.

Throwing himself into finding a solution, he has begun a partnership to finance and build experimental wind turbines locally, as well as develop and institute anaerobic digestive reactors. These devices use raw animal manure (of which the earth has an abundant supply) for energy production.

His dreams all started at the base level—with the tiniest of communities—his family and home garden. Roger knows that he has already made a difference in his neighborhood and set a green example for his son, Christian, to follow. Beautifying and enhancing the town he lives in by building gardens and donating bulbs will encourage positive economic growth for the community. By taking his dreams a step farther and giving the gift of alternative energy sources to the larger community, Quackenbush will set a positive environmental precedence for the world to follow.

Everyday Quackenbush throws his heart into making a difference and gives something priceless back to the community; hope for the future.

Emily Larson, Roger Quackenbush, and Marvin Miller are fantastic examples of people in the community who care and contribute to the greater good of humanity by starting small and gradually accomplishing community projects. They are just the beginning of a large group of wonderful, caring people who have made a personal difference in my life through a volunteer organization within my community. When I first began my journey to better health, I did not understand how intricately family and community are tied to feelings of self-worth and well-being. That is all changed now as I understand how community work can improve people's outlook on their own mental health. My message to you, the reader, has become stronger because of my own experience. It is time for you to build your community and give your time to the projects in your neighborhood that will make a positive difference for others.

Enriching my life emotionally was easy once I altered my lifestyle to include more than the TV as a social focus. This enlightenment can be yours also. All the people with whom I volunteer and build community say the same thing. They say that being involved in giving to and assisting others has helped them feel better about themselves and the way their lives are going. They feel more satisfied and filled with energy. They feel like they belong and can make a difference.

In fact, I have proven that one person can make a difference. Imagine what a whole community can do when working together for a common cause?

Greg Christian is making American meals healthier and greener

When I think of Greg Christian, I think of a passionate man who puts children first—his own as well as all youth, as they are the future of human kind. He is a man who cares about the environment and his neighborhood community with an equal fervor. Christian believes in doing what is right for the global population, and starting with the neighborhood community has been the best place to begin.

Christian is a Chicago-based professional chef with more than twenty years of experience who has started a revolution in healthy eating. He currently runs Greg Christian Catering, a firm that is on a mission to nourish with inventive, natural, and organic cuisine that will have an impact on the health of the population and a deep regard for the preservation and protection of our planet. Christian focuses on buying local foods to help curtail unnecessary energy use. His staff prepares foods which are hormone-free and organic—chemical and pesticide free—whenever possible.

The passionate desire Christian has to improve the nutritious quality of foods for his community led him to open Get Me Greg's Online Catering, which specializes in bringing his special green approach to offices throughout Chicagoland. Not only does he provide the freshest food possible, he also tries to change the mindset of the average office worker by providing recyclable dinnerware and biodegradable disposable flatware.

Christian got tired of the world talking about our and the environment's health, but not doing anything about it. "I want to see change," he zealously announces, "I see a lot of people talking, but very few people physically trying to make a difference for their community! It is time to see change and improvement, so I am doing something about it right now! I am making a difference!"

Greg Christian. Photo by Kristina Carter, Vrai Photography.

Indeed he is. On top of being one of the only green catering companies in the nation, Christian founded the Organic School Project (OSP). This project encourages American school-aged children to be more mindful eaters. His not-for-profit organization implemented and evaluated a wellness services model. Beginning with the 2006-2007 school year, he took this program into schools within the Chicago Public School System which is part of the third largest school district in the nation. OSP is teaching sustainability and mindful green habits at the grassroots level. They are accomplishing what some say is impossible, but Christian and his team persevere. Their model will make the dream of living healthier a reality by teaching children, from the very beginning of their education, what positive, chemical-free, nutrition means and its impact on our planet.

The OSP model has three major components: 1) reconnecting children with their food source through organic gardening, 2) teaching children nutrition, mindfulness, and environmental stewardship through a wellness curriculum, and 3) feeding the children more environmentally positive meals through the school system by encouraging made-from-scratch, organic, and natural foods which are sourced locally when seasonably available.

Greg Christian's inspiration and devotion to this project came from his youngest daughter. She battled chronic allergy-induced asthma throughout her childhood. With increasing frustration, Christian and his family tried to live with

the illness through traditional medical treatment. When this did not work and his daughter's health continued to worsen, he decided to try alternative medicine and an all-organic diet. This was a tremendous success. Since his daughter has been on an organic diet for almost ten years, her overall health has improved to such a startling degree that she no longer has any asthma attacks.

Discovering the difference organic foods made for his daughter motivated Christian deeply. He says, "I developed a general rule of thumb for food—the less machine-touched, the less machine-processed, the healthier it is and the more it will help the body."

Greg Christian teaching American school children about proper nutrition. Photo by Eric Hausman.

Christian began to realize that his life's work of cooking and catering could bring better health to thousands of people. This led to the idea of helping other children and ultimately building the OSP program. His concern about conservation, particularly in relationship to foods which go through long and difficult transportation processes, encouraged further research on purchasing local foods. He quickly realized that buying locally means far less resources are used, and the foods are riper, more nutritious, and taste better. He incorporated these ideas into the program as well, and the Organic School Project is now quite a success.

Greg Christian is preparing more nutritious locally grown dishes at his green-conscious catering company, Greg Christian Catering. Photo by Kristina Carter, Vrai Photography.

Christian's Catering team is doing one more thing—providing "green" details for every catering event He lists his food sources, distance traveled, amount of recyclable products, amount of water used, and which products were organic.

Here is an example of this incredible detail list is below:

Greg Christian Catering—Chicago's Conscious Caterer
Greening Events In Chicago
Host Event in Chicago
November 7 & 8

Greg Christian Catering featured products from twenty-one local area farms at both catered events. These farms included:

Growing Power Farms—IL—3 Miles*
* Rothkase Farm—WI—134 Miles
* Carr Valley—WI—212 Miles
* Mint Creek Farm—IL—88 Miles
* River Valley Ranch—WI—77 Miles
* Genesis Growers—IL—75 Miles
* Miller Amish Farm—IN—154 Miles
* Hidden Valley Farm—WI—174 Miles
* Greg Christian's Garden—IL—0 Miles
* Country Cottage Farm—IL—34 Miles
* Tipi Farms—WI—126 Miles
* Happy Valley Farms—WI—167 Miles
* Harmony Valley Farms—WI—246 Miles
* Smits Farm—IL—30 Miles

- Tranquility Bay Farm—WI—150 Miles
- Michigan Turkey Farmers—MI—175 Miles
- Crawford Farm—WI—147 Miles
- Tallgrass Beef—KS—682 Miles
- Green Acres—IN—90 Miles

*Food miles are the number of total miles it takes from source to end consumer. In the U.S., produce at the average grocery stores travels nearly 1,500 miles between the farms where it was grown and your refrigerator (SustainableTable.org). *

At Greg Christian Catering and Events we recycle for both catered and corporate events as well as in our kitchen and offices. All of our plates, forks, knives, spoons, napkins, and cups are made of biodegradable material.

Through the help of Ken Dunn, with the Resource Center in Chicago, our kitchen and offices have gone from 42 yards of waste a week to 5 yards.

The Resource Center, run by Ken Dunn, picked up the recycling and compost at both events. Once picked up and sorted, they weigh the items for documentation.

From the event on November 7 at Navy Pier with 1,750 guests, the Resource Center reported:

- 560 lbs of compost
- 700 lbs of glass
- 65 lbs of cardboard
- 21 lbs of aluminum cans
- 4 lbs of plastic

From the event on November 8 at The Merchandise Mart with 5,000 Guests, The Resource Center reported:

- 1,920 lbs of glass
- 2,840 lbs of compost
- 240 lbs of cardboard
- 12 lbs of aluminum Cans
- 26 lbs of plastic

At Greg Christian Catering and Events, we are committed to composting in order to keep food waste out of landfills. We also donate all of our used cooking oil to a local farm, FarmGirl Organics, for their biofuel car.

As a Chicago Conscious Caterer we donate all excess food to Chicago's Pacific Garden Mission. At both of these events, this service was not needed as all the food was consumed by guests and staff.

The Buffet Décor throughout the event was created with all living botanicals. The wandering jews, hand dried oak tree leaves, and organic bamboo that filled the buffets will be reused at future events. The décor involved no water waste. The passing trays also featured living botanicals which can be replanted into the ground after use, and the vegetables were used as food receptacles.

The bar was filled with organic wine, beer and soda. Each receptacle that was used at the bar was recycling or composted to its correct location.

Staff wore nametags that were collected at the duration of the evening to insure reuse of each plastic tag.

Menu cards and buffet signs were posted on recycled paper, and recognized each local farm with the specific miles.

For Greg Christian, being part of a community means helping that community become healthier. He believes in sharing his passion for being green and teaching others the importance of living a healthier and more mindful lifestyle. What does Christian see for the future? He has some exciting goals. He wants to see the OSP program practiced in every school in the nation. Christian says, "I want to see the world become more mindful. Wouldn't it be exciting to see every community in the United States band together to grow their own vegetables so we can bring more nutritious food to our children, which is more sustainable and uses less energy to produce? I believe that providing a healthier future for the children in every community should be a top concern for all of us."

Would you like to get closer to your community? Find ways to improve the quality of food for your local school children. Find ways to utilize foods which have been grown closer to your home. Think more about organic foods and the benefits they can bring your community—perhaps your neighborhood can start its own program. Start a vegetable garden which benefits your neighborhood and family.

Greg Christian wants the world to be mindful of foods and health. Greening your community is the first step to accomplish this thoughtful approach. Bring the people in your community together to follow Christian's exciting example of improving health by better nutrition and better greening.

Google; Setting A Community Example Of Bettering The Human Condition

One person can make a difference. But what if I told you that one corporation can make a difference as well? Improved mental and physical health is dependent upon this concept, and it applies to ongoing greening, better health, and community building as well as many other aspects of life. Google is a company filled with employees who are making a difference in all these categories.

Google founders, Larry Page and Sergey Brin. (Google photos © Google Inc. Used with permission.)

When founders, Larry Page and Sergey Brin began Google in a Stanford University dorm room, they had no idea Google would become a corporate cultural icon and a positive global influence. Since Google's initial incorporation in 1998, its influence has gone beyond the traditional American corporate mindset, setting new standards in "outside-the-box" thinking. The term "google" is even listed in the dictionary as a common reference to search for information online.

The Google way of thinking puts environmentalism, philanthropy, and positive employee relations at the forefront of their mission. In other words, for Google it is not just about the money, it is about bettering the human condition of their employees—and people everywhere. Testimony to this is in the commonly used unofficial Google slogan, "Don't be evil!"

At the forefront of this concept is an open management style which encourages idea contribution from all Google employees. According to Google, "The exchange of ideas is essential to creating a successful, collaborative working environment. We're organized into small, flat teams that allow for interaction between all employees, and we actively encourage all employees to ask questions, even to those at our highest levels. One example of this is our weekly TGIF meeting, which is hosted by Larry Page and Sergey Brin and gives all employees—even international employees, who can attend via videoconference and submit questions online—the chance to ask the founders any question they want, from large company-wide objectives to more mundane work questions."

Google CEO, Eric Schmidt, Ph.D.. (Google photos © Google Inc. Used with permission.)

The message that bettering one's self and one's community can go hand in hand with corporate business is a uniquely positive outlook in today's corporate world. Yet this is what Google CEO Eric Schmidt, Ph.D., encourages. When others said it was not possible, Google decided to "garden nude" on a global level, stating clearly that one company can make a difference for the world by building a community of do-gooders. In turn, if you ask any of the Google employees who have worked on a positive do-good project for the community how they feel about themselves, you will be rewarded with a surprisingly positive response. Why? Because doing good for others within a community improves attitudes and builds reassuring relationships. It makes people happy and healthy.

Google continues to set a positive example for the rest of the corporate world by developing ongoing programs to help their employees live a healthier and greener lifestyle. Simultaneously, Google is influencing employees to make a difference in the world by accomplishing do-good activities for people in their own communities as well as globally by setting an example for others to follow. This is a significant ingredient in building community.

Philanthropic efforts at Google come from all over the company, and are not just housed in Google.org [the philanthropic arm of Google corporate]. Several other efforts are underway at Google, from environmentally-focused initiatives to in-kind advertising for non-profits. These efforts start online at a community based website built to assist Google employees help the outside community.

According to CNNMoney.com, after the company's initial public offering (IPO) in August of 2004, founders

Google provides free meals for employees. (Google photos © Google Inc. Used with permission.)

Sergey Brin and Larry Page, as well as current CEO Dr. Eric Schmidt, requested that their base salary be cut to one dollar. They realized they already had a generous income from Google stock returns. Unlike many other corporate upper managers in the United States who want more and more and combine their excessively high salaries with stock returns, the senior Google team sees the reality—that enough is enough. They believe it is better to use the income for bettering employee working conditions or supporting programs that help others within the global community. They know that their stock benefits are tied directly to the performance of the company; and therefore, management's direct dedication to Google will be reflected in positive stock performance from stock returns. For senior management at Google, it is all about setting a positive example.

Working conditions, benefits, and corporate team-building experiences are excellent at Google. These positive experiences are considered "out-of-the-box benefits" compared to the average American business, and they help promote the unique family community environment in which Google employees revel. In other words, it encourages positive mental health.

Currently, all employees may receive free lunch, dinner, and snacks while working at a Google facility. These meals are served by world-class chefs. Dr. Taraneh Razavi, M.D. is the corporate on-site doctor for Google. She says that one of her main roles as the company doctor is education and prevention, "Google has been very good about setting up an environment which allows me to spend the time

Taraneh, Razavi, M.D.

necessary time with the patients to better educate them about the particular medical conditions rather than having to see them in the hurried manner that most clinics and doctors have to conduct their practices. The employees feel that they have an advocate."

This is a particularly advantageous situation for Google employees as having an on-site doctor can enhance early detection of health issues, therefore promoting and encouraging better physical health. Razavi says, "Being physically present in the work atmosphere has allowed me to better analyze the needs of the workers and to assess what types of programs such as nutrition, smoking cessation or weight loss plans, for example, should be implemented. In general, I see the same types of medical conditions that I would see in an outside office—hypertension, diabetes, high cholesterol—however, I see these conditions much earlier than I normally would as an outside doctor because the employees/ patients are more likely to come in sooner to see me at work than they would if they had to make an appointment and spend a few hours outside of work. This is important, because early diagnosis and intervention in management of these patients have a significant impact in the long term morbidity and mortality outcome."

A special mental health benefit of working with Google is the company allows employees to bring dogs to work. Pets are great stress relievers. Google recognizes

that dogs can be a valuable and important part of employees' lives, and one that can greatly enhance employees' overall work experience. The presence of dogs at Google has always been a unique and treasured part of our workplace culture.

The list of benefits extends from employee referral programs to more than fifteen days paid vacation each year. As a

A dog enjoying time spent with his master at the Google facility. (Google photos © Google Inc. Used with permission.)

California Google employee, if your regularly scheduled child care cancels, Google provides up to five free days of child care each year. Employees may tap into many utilitarian on-site services at the corporate headquarters, including oil change, car wash, dry cleaning, massage therapy, gym, hair stylist, fitness classes, and bike repair, just to name a few.

To encourage philanthropy, Google has a wonderful program. The company will match any donations an employee gives to a nonprofit organization, up to $3,000 each year. Google's many family assistance programs help build the family community, including adoption assistance or maternity leave for both parents of a newborn. Google's goal is to build a group of healthy employees who can contribute by doing good for both their family community and the global community.

Google has far exceeded any humble goals the founding team dreamed of financially, but Google's true wealth is in how it is inspiring others to be greener and healthier around the world.

Google built a corporate community which has become like a second family to many of its employees, referred to as "Googlers." With more than 16,000 of the most creative and talented employees in the world, Google recognizes the possible positive influence they may have on all of humanity worldwide. What an amazing statement that is now becoming a reality.

In 2007, Google made an exciting announcement that, for 2007 and all years moving forward, the company will be carbon neutral. Google's giant computer infrastructure must be housed in buildings which need to be cooled and managed. Bolstering power-saving technologies, such as evaporative cooling systems, has increased the efficiency of the company's data centers. Reducing the corporate carbon footprint by replacing incandescent bulbs with high-efficiency lighting as

Google's Mountain View campus with solar panels shining. (Google photos © Google Inc. Used with permission.)

well as utilizing natural light is a common practice at Google facilities. The Mountain View, California, headquarters currently has one of the largest solar panel installations in the United States.

Remarkable and amazing you say? Not for Google. These do-good-for-the-community policies are just the beginning of how Google is making a difference for the family-like employee community. Several examples of how Google encourages its employees to go a step above and beyond to improve health and build community is documented on the Official Google Blog. Community building efforts for 2008 include a health push at the Atlanta Google office. Googlers partnered with the Parks, Recreation and Historic Sites Division of the Georgia Department of Natural Resources to support an initiative called Get Outdoors Georgia (GO Georgia). Google Transit is explained on the blog page as well, an initiative which helps the average American plan trips using public transportation.

Google provides a lengthy online list of green tools for both professional and residential computer users. Providing this free information helps expand greening knowledge for the average citizen and how it can touch each community.

Also, as part of the company's ongoing initiatives to reduce carbon emissions and encourage healthier breathing quality for its employees, encourages physical exercise and utilization of non-carbon emitting products. As an example, many Googlers bike to work. According to Joe Gross, a systems operation manager at Google, "So many Googlers commute by bike every day that you can't easily look down a hallway and not see a bicycle or two leaning against the wall. Some people bike in from just a few miles away while others combine their commute with other [physical] training."

In an ongoing effort to improve transportation and build community traffic flow, Google provides courtesy bikes for employees both at the Mountain View, California, and European locations. These bikes help pedestrians get from one side of a campus to the other without using of carbon output transportation. Further programs include an employee shuttle program, alternative fuel vehicle fleet, and other environmental transportation programs.

Google team members told me that at the Mountain View headquarters that community 'GBikes' are accessible to all employees, allowing an efficient and enjoyable manner during the work day. Green-friendly Googlers can also bike or take public transportation to work with the Self-Powered Commuting Program (which offers a donation to a charity of choice for each day of travel). The goal, of course, is to reduce carbon output, but it is also to facilitate a better community plan which enables pedestrians to both safely traverse facilities and utilize healthy building and community enhancing tools with which to do so.

This consideration from larger corporations, such as Google, is particularly important for Americans. At the Chicagoland Metropolitan Council's Conference in 2007 titled, "The Heat is On: Why hybrid vehicles won't save the planet", Reid Ewing, Ph.D. spoke about the need for greening to include more than recycling and alternative vehicle choices. His presentation centered on the concept that when corporations and cities engineer road and structural layout to avoid urban sprawl conditions, it is more convenient to live a greener lifestyle, and therefore, easier to be healthier. For example, less carbon is used when a car needs to travel a shorter distance. People walk more when retail stores and services are closer to one's home or office.

Reid Ewing, Ph.D.

Ewing, with his contemporaries, published a groundbreaking article in the American Journal of Health Promotion. Titled "Relationship between urban sprawl and physical activity, obesity, and morbidity" the article is based on a study where researchers determined the relationship between urban sprawl, health, and health-related issues. Their conclusions surprised the scientific community when they discovered a direct correlation between obesity and communities with poor urban planning and land transportation management. Google is one of the first businesses in the world to address this concern by engineering and building transportation systems and facility layout which encourage interactive community exercise and convenient low-emission vehicles for their employees.

Building a better, greener community can connect mental health, physical health, and the satisfaction level of the people living within that community. Google has figured out that enhancing a person's lifestyle is not simply about handing an employee a salary. Rather, it is more significant to help that employee live a better quality of life and achieve day-to-day satisfaction in life's journey. The company has learned that many things are involved in finding satisfaction in life. From the physical layout of the corporate facilities, to providing programs which encourage better mental and physical health, to encouraging a more mindful way of looking at the world.

While Google won the prestigious award of being the best employer to work for in the Fortune Magazine's 2008 list of top 100 employers, this seems a small achievement compared to the monumental global community good Google is doing.

Larry Brilliant, M.D. (Google photos © Google Inc. Used with permission.)

Larry Brilliant, M.D. is currently the executive director at Google.org, the philanthropic arm of the Google organization built to care for the world. Global challenges, such as climate change, poverty, and emerging disease are addressed aggressively. Google.org is challenging itself and the world to improve living conditions for all of humanity—the ultimate community. Tapping into the power of modern day information and technology, Brilliant and his team hope to empower people around the world with five major initiatives: Develop Renewable Energy Cheaper Than Coal (RE<C), RechargeIT, Predict and Prevent, Inform and Empower to Improve Human Services, and Fuel the Growth of Small and Medium-Sized Enterprises.

Renewable Energy Cheaper Than Coal Initiative (RE<C) is a fantastic plan to improve the global community's energy needs. This strategic initiative is researching development of electricity from renewable resources that are cheaper to produce than coal. Initially, the focus is on solar thermal power, wind power and enhanced geothermal technologies. Coal still provides nearly 40 percent of the world's electricity. If successful, the RE<C program could provide solutions which can significantly reduce global carbon emissions from coal burning, and improve the air quality for millions of people across the world.

Google has joined the Climate Savers Computing Initiative (CSCI). According to the CSCI website, "By 2010, we seek to reduce global CO2 emissions from the operation of computers by 54 million tons per year, equivalent to the annual output of 11 million cars or 10 to20 coal-fired power plants. This effort will lead to a 50 percent reduction in power consumption by computers by 2010, and committed participants could collectively save $5.5 billion in energy costs."

Accelerating the adoption of plug-in hybrid electric vehicles and vehicle-to-grid technology, RechargeIT targets carbon emissions. Google, utilizing the expression "practice what you preach," proves to demonstrate that businesses should be the first ones in a community to set a positive environmental example. Leading the

Demonstrating a RechargeIt vehicle, Dr. Larry Brilliant shows that it is easy to use. (Google photos (c) Google Inc. Used with permission.)

way, the company demonstrates this technology within its own fleet and supports others by providing grants and investments to revolutionize the "plug-in" mindset.

Google.org has a special leader in Dr. Larry Brilliant. He was one of the doctors who helped eradicate small pox from our planet. He founded the Seva Foundation, a nonprofit organization that cured approximately two million people of blindness in more than fifteen countries. In 2006, Brilliant won the TED Prize, a remarkable award given by The Sapling Foundation. The TED organization encourages and fosters a better understanding of the issues facing the world and bonds the world community to create a more positive future. When Brilliant won the TED prize, in addition to the $100,000 he received from the foundation, he was also granted "one wish to change the world". This wish allowed him to ask some of the greatest minds on earth to help him build a global early-response system to detect new diseases or disasters as quickly as they emerge or occur. When instituted, perhaps this seemingly impossible wish will eradicate the enormous potential of a pandemic disease threat. Shortly after Brilliant won this award, he was invited by Google executives to manage Google.org and help a company filled with do-gooders make a serious difference in the world community.

Predict and Prevent is a direct response to Brilliant's vision of a pandemic-free world. Google.org's utilization of information and technology to assist in the prediction and prevention of emerging disasters and threats on a local, regional, and global level could change the face of humanity. Its early spotlight will be infectious diseases, which are on the rise worldwide.

Google.org established the Inform and Empower To Improve Human Services program in a humanitarian effort to improve public services globally, such as clean water, education, and health systems. As communities come together to build stronger accountability, it will help change the quality of public services throughout the world.

Many developing countries suffer from poor economic growth. Often, this is because the government does not support small and middle-sized business growth which would benefit small communities. By funding these businesses, the Fuel The Growth of Small and Medium Sized Enterprises (SMEs) program seeks to reduce poverty in communities which desperately need the tools and knowledge to improve their living conditions.

All of these Google.org programs do something special for our world; they help bring people together. This creates better mental and physical health—this is the message of this book. Building community is so much more than simply knowing and waving at your neighbors. Building community is about creating stronger avenues to help build a better world.

Most everyone in the world must work in one form or another to support their families. Ultimately, all of these workers must report to their supervisor who is, most often, a part of a corporation. Millions of corporations have millions of workers which all unite to supply the earth with its many needs. Although companies often supply workers with a pay check and insurance, the companies seldom supply a comprehensive plan to assist workers understand the greater world like Google demonstrates.

There are many reasons to begin corporate programs that focus on well being and community. It is important to build these programs where you work. Why? By starting from the ground up and building community within a corporation, it improves employee's mental and physical health. Business will soon see that they can ensure a more productive work output. More importantly, the employees will soon see that it is much easier to come to work when you feel as if you are a part of a family community within your working environment. You feel less stressed and more mentally healthy.

Instituting a corporate program might also be the spark to motivate the business' global contribution to greening and health practices. Once the program is understood, it will soon become evident that world health can be improved as well as an individual employee's health. Google and Google.org are evidence that a single corporation can make a global difference and inspire positive actions from its smaller employee community.

In the end, contributing to employees' health can become a catalyst for positive change within employees' personal lives. It can set an example to each and every employee that the company holds high expectations for beneficial health practices. This concept can expand exponentially if the employees utilize the healthier greening and living ideas promoted by the company and then proceed to teach their families and neighborhood communities these same ways of living.

Soon it becomes far more than a way to improve production within the business; it demonstrates and encourages "doing the right thing" mentality.

Imagine, if every business within the United States picked up this idea of supporting their employees—their corporate community—by educating them on better health practices, greening practices, and community building techniques? The concept seems revolutionary, yet the implications of building a better, greener world by utilizing corporate entities is awesome! And yes, it can help contribute to better world health.

Part IV—
The Good Life
Manifesto

---

*"It seems to me that the good life
is not any fixed state. It is not, in my
estimation, a state of virtue, or contentment,
or nirvana, or happiness.
The good life is a process, not a state of being.
It is a direction not a destination."*

—CARL ROGERS, PH.D., *ON BECOMING A PERSON*

I	S	#	S	A	T	I	S
#	?	E	3	N	2	Z	F
E	H	A	O	O	T	V	Y
F	E	C	T	W	;	=	I
I	L	H	H	%	+	9	N
L	P	%	E	X	6	4	G
#	7	1	R	8	Y	?	#
D	O	O	G	#	E	H	T

Chapter Twelve

The Good Life Manifesto—Inspiration

∞

I f you have learned anything from this book, I want it to be that you CAN lead a life filled with satisfaction and feeling good. You can live a more satisfied and healthier life—remember, it is not about achieving perfect health or a perfect body weight—it is about being mindful of your lifestyle so you can feel better both mentally and physically.

The Good Life Manifesto is testimony to the fact that you *can* do this! My discovery of *The Good Life Manifesto* happened by watching my grandparents model their lifestyles for me. When I was a little girl, I lived in a rural area of central Indiana. I grew up within a complicated "Yours, Mine and Ours" family (which seems to be the common family type these days). I had three grandmothers. Each was unique in attitude and mindset and shared a commonality as well; a desire to do the right thing. To live a more mindful way in a complex and ever changing world is not easy, and my grandmothers were far from perfect. They had very human faults, yet they were immensely healthy and satisfied people. All my grandmothers, for instance, lived to be over 80. Learning to accept and like their individuality as well as accepting what life handed them made them stronger and healthier individuals. Each knew she had a unique place in the community which she helped build. Accepting who we are for what we are as well as trying to do the right thing—every day—is an important concept I want the readers of this book to understand and take to heart.

It might seem difficult to achieve at first, but I am not asking you, the reader, to do anything I have not attempted or experienced myself. Achieving a more mindful lifestyle is a positive step forward for you, as it has been for me. The decisions I have made in life have not always been the best. Sometimes I have fallen down and made mistakes. When I was younger, these moments were frequently painful learning experiences. As I have grown, however, I see the value in trying my best to emulate my grandmothers' mindset and live a lifestyle which is as positive as I can make it.

All three grandmothers nurtured nature and, in there own ways, let me know that their lives were more satisfactory because of the time they spent communing in one form or another with the outdoors. There were a few unspoken rules each of them followed which led to a healthy attitude and strong emotional strength.

This helped pull them through most any stress they came up against. Those unspoken rules are important, and I describe them with *The Good Life Manifesto*.

Our grandparents were educated by *their* parents on life and nature. Their parents, our distant ancestors, grew up in a time of war and lived a life when everyone had to conserve and be mindful simply to survive. They all modeled the Manifesto rules to their children, before the concepts of greening, conservation, and eco-friendly were ever popular. These rules apply today as always, because they are, as they were then, *the right thing to do*.

Fundamentally, the gardening nude concept is based roughly on the powerful influence of these rules. I believe success for good health can be found by considering *The Good Life Manifesto* in conjunction with the *Get Your Green On Healthy Philosophy*.

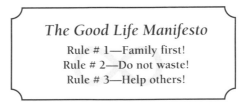

The Good Life Manifesto
Rule # 1—Family first!
Rule # 2—Do not waste!
Rule # 3—Help others!

These rules are simple. As I see it, rule Number One points to having strong emotional health. Rule Number Two speaks to conservation and taking care of the Earth. Rule Number Three addresses the need to be a part of a community and care for the people within that community. This is what the *Get Your Green On Healthy Philosophy* touches on as well. Living by these rules, my grandmothers were satisfied and happy individuals.

Grandma Ruthadell and Grandpa with Shawna in the early 1970's.

The education I received from my grandmothers has left an indelible mark on my life about what is important. It was nearly two decades after I left my grandmothers and their beautiful, green, fertile, countryside that I finally understood the message they wanted me to learn.

Grandma Ruthadell

It was the '70's, and I was six years old when my father was remarried to Ruthadell's daughter, Linda. Every weekend we traipsed out to Grandma Ruthadell's farm for a sleepover and Sunday dinner. She and Grandpa raised corn, soybeans, wheat, and hogs. An older man, who was a farm helper, lived in a spare bedroom upstairs in their 100-

year-old farmhouse. For free food, free rent, and a little cash, he helped Grandpa manage the property and animals.

Grandma was an excellent cook who made lots of southern favorites using food fresh from her garden. Her girth spoke to lots of food sampling while she was cooking, and she had an efficient way about her whether in the kitchen or in the garden. She enjoyed building relationships in the community and making others feel good by her loving efforts. She often fixed dinner dishes for nearby families who might be going through a difficult time. If someone needed help, Grandma was there to give it.

Grandma was more of a vegetable gardener than a flower gardener, probably because she was practical. She worked to help feed the family with both profits from the larger farmland and the produce from the family garden. The large vegetable garden included sweet corn, peas, green beans, tomatoes, zucchini, watermelon, and pumpkins. At age six, I was thrilled to plant the seeds for Grandma. One year, sunflowers were my favorite, and I was amazed they grew over six feet tall. In this fashion—learning from example—I was educated on the true source of more nutritious food. It came from the soil I touched and planted in. Hogs provided hams and other meat for our plate. I now grow sunflowers and tomatoes with my children.

Most everything that could be grown on the farm was utilized in some way, even the flowers. On Memorial Day Grandma believed in giving back to the community by expressing her respect for the family and friends who died through the military. She had the loveliest pink peony flowers blooming in May and we were all put to work gathering dozens of them. Grandma would drawl in her Southern accent, "It's time to cut the 'pine-ees' and take'em to the cemetery." We put them in recycled foil wrapped coffee cans filled with water and leave them on the

Old fashioned peony in bloom.

memorials of friends and family. Ordering flower memorials from a flower shop was never considered, as this would be wasteful and expensive when she already had the flowers to donate.

By the time I was nine, Grandpa had died and Grandma could no longer maintain the garden or her farm. After my father had passed away, my Mother and I moved to live with Grandma to help her with the farm. One of the most significant things about Grandma Ruthadell was that she would give a person in need most anything to help them. She helped the community. Some would say this generosity and kindness is naïve or pretentious, but I say that is untrue: we should all try to be giving and helpful to the community. It builds people up emotionally. It is needed. She spent her life dedicated to *The Good Life Manifesto* without ever realizing it. Grandma knew what was right and doing what was right was important to her, as it should be to all of us.

Grandma Mabel

My father's mother was Grandma Mabel. A tiny woman with an Irish heritage; she wore size one shoes and stood well beneath five feet tall. Grandma had sparkling blue eyes, her hair was perpetually white, and she always had a smile and kind word for everyone. She was mother to five children and taught them all a strong work ethic and the love of music and books.

Grandma grew many things at her clean, white-washed farm when it was fully operational, including a full vegetable garden and chickens. However, by the time I came around, the farm had stopped producing. Her vegetable garden, from which she had grown and canned to help support her family, had been given up long ago. Grandma did not have a traditional garden when I was a part of her life, but she gifted me with her knowledge. She had large fields and pastures of country meadow. I remember climbing trees, walking fences, and riding ponies through

Shawna's Grandma Mabel (right) and Aunt Loretta (left)

pastures of green grass with my cousins while she watched over us. We picked mulberries until our hands were stained and our tummies ached. This exposure to the natural world helped my mind develop. Many children today have not walked through a field or pasture. They have not experienced the sound of grass waving in the wind. This must change. Children must not be afraid to go outdoors and experience the healthy benefits of nature.

Grandma knew every herb, medicinal plant, and dozens of wildflowers by their country name. As we walked through flowering fields, she would tell me

which plants were poisonous, helpful, or simply beautiful. Sometimes we would harvest the plants and she would dry them. It was a delight for me that she cared enough to teach me the details. Although her garden was not traditional like others I knew; its content seemed far wealthier. I now know why; this kind of outdoor exposure was essential for me to have and is critical for the children of our communities to experience. Having emotional security and confidence can often be traced back to our childhood experiences in nature.

Queen Anne's Lace from an Indiana prairie.

My favorite nature activity with Grandma was picking white Queen Anne's Lace to put in a vase in her kitchen. We'd color the water red with food coloring and, within a day, the white flowers would change a lively red. When I was small that simple act was nothing short of a miracle. To Grandma it was a science lesson I needed to understand and learn. She felt it was important to teach your children the way of the world, from the simplest flower to the most complex issue. Everything was a lesson with Grandma and she taught the lessons with a slyness that belied her sweet nature. She knew the best way to teach was to lead by example instead of giving a lecture. Being satisfied with what you have—not always demanding more—and living a healthy life is something I watched her do. Grandma Mabel's way of teaching—by getting outdoors and truly experiencing it—is something our modern day children desperately need exposure to.

In my mind, because of Grandma Mabel, a garden is definitively more than a "traditional" perennial bed or a place to grow vegetables. It is a natural school, a place to relax and play, to learn about life and be healthy. Grandma Mabel never wasted or polluted the natural environment. She recycled most everything and taught me to do so also. She reused foil baking dishes, paper, building material, even mouse traps. Everything was all washed with lots of soap and used again and again.

Grandma Mabel died over fifteen years ago, within a few days of the birth of my first child, but her love continues in my heart. Her practical inspiration has stayed with me my entire life. She taught me that life is what you make of it and the natural environment is a precious thing not to be harmed. Hard work produces results, and being healthy depends on a conserving mind set.

Grandma Mildred

My third grandmother, Grandma Mildred, was my natural mother's mother. She lived well into her nineties, and was very intelligent, cultured, well-spoken and strong-minded. Her sense of humor was fantastic; her sense of the natural environment and conserving was an intricate part of her life. She lived on a farm most of her life, like my other Grandmothers, but possessed a unique sense of the greater world at large, which made her stand apart from many women of her era.

This photo features Shawna with her Grandma Mildred and Grandpa Joe at their Indiana farm.

All the grandchildren called our grandmother "Maudie" instead of Grandma Mildred. We were thrilled to learn from her and loved to spend time with her. Although our parents were all divorced, my half-sisters and I would come out to her farm several times a year because Maudie insisted that she have visitation privileges with each and every one of us. She did this because she believed in building community by putting family first—a key part of The Good Life Manifesto. This maternal modeling left a very strong impression on the entire group of children who adored her.

She lived in a beautiful brick farm house with Grandpa Joe. Before retirement she worked at a courthouse demonstrating her hard-edged progressive belief that women can and should have a career of their choice. She insisted that "women can do *anything* men can do!" Maudie volunteered at the local hospital for many years during her retirement. She felt that giving back to the community is an important part of a human being's contribution to community. She believed in hard work and doing a job the right way, not the easy way. If we did not do a job she assigned us right, she would shove us out of the way and show us exactly how it was supposed to be done. We learned it is better to do it right the first time.

Maudie was born and raised in the country and continued to farm and garden most of her life, she believed trees were very important to the world and was a stalwart arborist. Maudie was the first person to explain to me that trees are important for conservation; they keep our homes and neighborhoods cool in the summer and protected in the winter. This environmental attitude, along with her on-going dedication to gardening, was quite an influence on me through out my life. She was so dedicated to trees that, when I was young, I romantically thought

Grandma Mildred with Shawna at age four.

of Maudie as someone like Julia Butterfly Hill who wrote *The Legacy of Luna* and camped out in a redwood tree for over two years to save its life. Maudie was far more practical minded than that I suppose, but her love of trees infected me at a very early age none-the-less.

I remember a conversation I had with Maudie when I was perhaps ten years old when she shared with me her concerns about the Earth's overpopulation, which is an environmental and conservation-centered issue that plagues all of us on Earth. We were standing on her front porch watching a particularly gorgeous sunset over the quiet Indiana fields. It was awe-inspiring for me to see the bright oranges and flaming reds fill the sky. I remember telling her that I loved her farm because it helped feed people all across the world.

She looked at me pointedly and replied, "No, Shawna. It is nothing so romantic. My farm is very small compared to the needs of the world. You see, there's a population explosion happening. Imagine if all your generation has four children and all their children have four children, and all their children have four children, what will happen to the world? I know many families nearby who have six children or more. How will we feed them all on the small land existing here on this planet?"

Continuing, she said, "There are many problems; people do not consider birth control a choice. Many people are irresponsible and have more children than they can emotionally or financially handle. What's wrong with having two children or less? I think most people would be better parents and they would use far less resources so the Earth's land would be able to feed people adequately. It's difficult to feed and clothe a large family. How will my great-great grandchildren survive in a world that is filled to capacity? Each person must have time for themselves and a space for themselves here where we live. It is very difficult to do that when it is overcrowded. People need to think of the results of their actions before they perform them."

The sun had fallen below the horizon when she finished talking, so it was dark and the lightning bugs had come out. I thought on that conversation about the planet's health and our health for a long time while watching the tiny lightning bugs flicking on and off, and I still think about it today. Maudie was well into her sixties when she had that talk with me and it was one of the most profound conversations I have ever had. I am glad she was aware and hope that I am also able to teach my children that being healthy is far more than taking vitamins and practicing an exercise routine. We need to understand the health and future of the planet we live on and imagine what the future might be for our children if we continue living life without thinking through the consequences of our actions.

In Al Gore's book, *An Inconvenient Truth* he mentions that, when the United States was formed, the world population was around 1 billion. Currently the world population is approximately 6.5 billion, and by 2050 the world population is predicted to be about 9.1 billion. My grandmother had the foresight to see that the health of the world would hinge on this population growth and the possible destruction it would cause.

Maudie taught me that women can and should be intelligent, strong, determined, and opinionated. A woman can be a leader. She made it clear that all people can make a difference for the world by making choices on how to run their families' health and education. She was a rock in her community and an example to all of us. Maudie also lived her life with beauty and grace surrounding her, and felt it was critical for a healthy mind. She once told me the old adage, "Everything worth having is hard work." I believe that and live my life now by those words. Her family, her gardens, her trees, her nature—they were all birthed through very hard work which helped her live a healthier, longer, and more richly satisfying life. This one woman committing herself to *The Good Life Manifesto* rule of family first made a significant impression on my life and changed my attitude about the world. One person can make a difference; she made a difference.

So finally, long after all of my grandmothers have passed away, I understand the healthy living message they were trying to give me those many years ago. Our grandparents chose to live what some consider a simpler life than we do now with far less stress. Yet by living that way they truly led the good life.

My grandmothers and the mentality which guided all of them can be summed up simply in *The Good Life Manifesto*. To be healthy is to be mindful about yourself, your family and the world.

Living the "good life" is possible; you have to make the effort to make it a reality. You can make a difference.

Epilogue

"Always do right; this will gratify some people and astonish the rest."

—A NOTE TO THE YOUNG PEOPLE'S SOCIETY, GREENPOINT PRESBYTERIAN CHURCH, 1901, FROM MARK TWAIN

∞

And so now we come to the end of this book and the beginning of your journey to better health!

The reason I wrote this book is because I want to inspire more people to live a healthy lifestyle. Imagine the world as I do: a world filled with less stress, less depression, less cruelty, and less suffering. A world filled with far more kindness and good health. A greener and more caring world for our children to live in. A giving world!

No one knows more than I do the emotional and physical trauma life can deal out, but it is important to remember that nearly everyone has a hard luck story at one point in their life or another. If I had let a difficult youth, a traumatic health history, a divorce, and all the problems I have ever faced define me, then I would be living—but that is all I would be doing—existing. Being satisfied in life is more rewarding than any person could have explained to me.

Do not let the abusive people in the world attack your mental health! Do not let the doubters in to your heart! Do not give up on having a healthy lifestyle, no matter what your age or history! Hard luck stories prevail no matter your ethnic background or financial status or where you live. It is the tale of humanity. It is now the tale of the world. We must not let negative mindsets deter us from giving our children and our world the greater gift of health and caring.

The negative and uncaring way we have treated the world is a testimony to the fact that more people who live here need to have positive attitudes and a caring mindset. Earth is screaming out the truth that we must get greener in our lives or the caring mother that supports us will rebel. More people need to live healthier lifestyles to make a positive change for the world. You are responsible for your body and mind, not your spouse, nor your children, nor your medical doctors. You can make a difference and live a more satisfactory life in your community, but *you have to want to work towards success.*

I want this book to inspire a positive change for you so you can rid yourself of the emotional baggage, the Freudian resistance, the stress issues, and learn to "garden nude." In learning how to claim back your and the environments health, you will extend your reach far beyond what you imagined and touch other lives. It is especially important to learn to share and give to others. You can. You MUST. The choice seems clear that you cannot let the set-backs in life, your personal hard luck story, destroy the hope of giving the special person that you are to the world.

It is simple to understand—it can be you against the world endlessly fighting and struggling, or it can be you with your arms wrapped around the world building and nurturing.

Please stand up and open the front door. Go outside. Strip away the baggage and conquer the naysayers. Take a deep breath and jump into being healthy!

You CAN make a difference! You CAN garden nude!

Acknowledgements

Creating a book is a giant undertaking. I feel strongly compelled to acknowledge and thank the people who have helped me bring my unique vision to the world.

An immense thank you goes to Luis Coronado—genius, husband, and soul supporter. He has, in fact, been responsible for loving, goading, chasing, massaging, pressuring, pushing, and pulling me into good health. He has done this, not because he is overly healthy himself, but because he cares for me and wants me to live a satisfied life. Luis has shown me that to be satisfied in life is an immeasurable gift. This discovery is so significant to me that I want to "pay it forward" to as many human beings as I can, and hope I have begun to do so with this book.

Thanks go to my family, especially my two incredibly intelligent and strong-minded daughters, who have been constant sources of inspiration and joy. Their love and support means everything to me. When I felt down and frustrated when writing a difficult passage, they were the one's that shouted, "never give up!"

My parents, Linda and Donald Riggle, taught me from an early age that hard work is critical in life—this book was certainly hard work—and worth all the effort. My mother-in-law, Delores Coronado, inspired me to down-size, spend more time with my husband and beautiful children, and do something with my life which I truly love and believe in. She told me, "if you're happy in life, your family will be too." I believe that and am grateful. Thanks also go to my dear Aunt Loretta Bennett who insisted I write a book and would not take no for an answer!

My close friends, JuliAnn Bock and Big Jim Kleinwachter, have been indispensible in both supporting me and kicking me in the fanny (repeatedly). Their advice, love, and concern have been a gift. Samara Sears, Lisa Stitt, Pam Shaner, Brent Jordan, Barbara Walton, Dale Simpson, Jr., as well as Mike Vester and the Broken Vegas gang are just a few of the special friends and family who have touched me and the concept of gardening nude with such significant concern and inherent judgment, I would have been lost without their encouragement.

Very special thanks go to Dr. Nirmala Arora and Dr. Vipal Arora for supporting me and my family through more than ten years of difficult health struggles. Your patience and knowledge has been a wonderful contribution to my soul and to this book.

Dorothy Deer has been a true friend, as well as a ruthless and magnificent editor; chopping, grammatically correcting, and kindly suggesting her way through the entire manuscript. I could not have done this without her educated guidance and persistent help.

The medical and scientific experts referenced in this book responded to my research. They encouraged me, each and every one of them, in the most positive of ways, to continue with my distinctive ideas for the book and bring them to fulfillment. Thank you ALL.

For many years I have been writing an environmental, healthy gardening, and greening column titled, *The Casual Gardener.* My local community and column fans have been my testing ground for many of the concepts in this book and have cheered me on with such vigor and love I feel I owe them much gratitude as they have been tending this healthy garden of information with me. Thank you! Thank you! Every email, every letter, every kind word is appreciated. Please keep them coming!

The organizations I have been a part of in the community are filled with supportive, loving people who have given me advice and a hug when I needed it most. There are so many, many others that have been a part of this book in one way or another. I have spent countless hours at the public library researching and double-checking the facts I have contained in this book. Every one of the people at the Public Library in Warrenville, Illinois who helped me find those details deserves a thank you. I could not have done it alone.

Once again, I have turned to my community. All of you have shared a small part of yourself with me. Because of that I have been able to share my vision for a healthier lifestyle with the world.

Thank you for making a difference.

Appendix—Resources

This section contains resources and reference material. All resources are current as of the printing of this book and I hope they will help you. The resources listed below are not affiliated with me in any way, beyond the fact I have used the resources myself and feel they might be of assistance to you in your search for improved health and greening.

Information on Building Communities
WEBSITES:

America In Bloom—www.americainbloom.org

Habitat For Humanity—www.habitat.org

The University of Illinois Landscape and Human Health Laboratory—www.lhhl.uiuc.edu

Information on Conservation, the Environment and Nature

An Inconvenient Truth, The Planetary Emergency Of Global Warming And What We Can Do About It, By Al Gore, Rodale, 2006

Kane County Wild Plants & Natural Areas, By Dick Young, Kane County Forest Preserve District, Kane County, Illinois

Last Child In The Woods, By Richard Louv, Algonquin Books, 2006

The Legacy of Luna, The Story Of A Tree, A Woman, and The Struggle To Save The Redwoods, By Julia Butterfly Hill, HarperCollins, 2000

The Revenge of Gaia, Earth's Climate Crisis & The Fate Of Humanity, By James Lovelock, Basic Books, 2006

The Ten Trusts, What We Must Do To Care For The Animals We Love, By Jane Goodall & Marc Bekoff, HarperCollins, 2002.

The Wisdom of Wilderness, Experiencing the Healing Power of Nature, By Gerald G. May, HarperCollins, 2006

True Green, 100 Everyday Ways You Can Contribute To A Healthier Planet, By Kim McKay and Jenny Bonnin, National Geographic, 2006

What the River Knows, An Angler In Midstream, By Wayne Fields, University of Chicago Press, 1996

WEBSITES:

An Inconvenient Truth home website—www.climatecrisis.net

Arbor Day Foundation—www.arborday.org

Buy Recycled Government website—www.epa.gov/msw/buyrec.htm

Carnegie Mellon Green Practices for Campus Activity website—www.cmu.edu/greenpractices/index.html

Chicago Wilderness Consortium—www.chicagowilderness.org

Climate Savers Computing Initiative—www.climatesaverscomputing.org

Conservation @ Home Website Fact Sheets—
www.theconservationfoundation.org/index.php?option=com_content&task=view&id=91&Itemid=48

Energy Star Light Bulb Disposal Information—www.epa.gov/bulbrecycling

EPA's Dump No Waste In The Stormdrain Website—
http://www.epa.gov/adopt/patch/html/guidelines.html

EPA's Recycle City website—www.epa.gov/recyclecity

Fermi National Accelerator Laboratory's Natural Areas -
www.fermilabnaturalareas.com

Google Corporate Green Energy plan—
www.google.com/corporate/green/energy

Home Energy Saving Website—http://hes.lbl.gov/hes/vh.shtml

Land and Watershed Information—www.theconservationfoundation.org

National Environmental Directory—www.environmentaldirectory.net

National Wildlife Federation—www.nwf.org

Nike Reuse a Shoe/Nike Grind Program—www.letmeplay.com/reuseashoe

Recycling Is Working EPA website—www.epa.gov/jtr/econ/rei-rw/pdf/factsheet_nat.pdf

S.C.A.R.C.E. (School and Community Assistance for Recycling & Composting Education)—www.bookrescue.org

Share Your Soles shoe donation program—www.shareyoursoles.org

The University of Illinois Landscape and Human Health Laboratory—
www.lhhl.uiuc.edu

We Campaign—www.wecansolveit.com

World's Shortest Comprehensive Recycling Guide—
www.obviously.com/recycle/guides/shortest.html

Information on Gardening and Landscape Design
WEBSITES:

Hope In Bloom—www.hopeinbloom.org

Naomi Sachs Design—www.naomisachsdesign.com

Therapeutic Landscapes Database—www.healinglandscapes.org

The Casual Gardener Website and newspaper column database—
www.thecasualgardener.com

Tulips N More bulb supply [Roger Quackenbush's store]—
www.tulipsnmore.com

Information on Giving, Philanthropy, and Community

Giving, How Each Of Us Can Change The World, by Bill Clinton, Alfred A. Knopf, 2007

What the River Knows, An Angler In Midstream, By Wayne Fields, University of Chicago Press, 1996

Mother Teresa: In My Own Words, By Mother Teresa, Gramercy, 1997

WEBSITES:

Google.org—www.google.org

Habitat for Humanity—www.habitat.org

Range of Motion Project—www.rompglobal.org

Seva Foundation—www.seva.org

TED (Technology, Industry, Design)—www.ted.com

William J. Clinton Foundation—www.clintonfoundation.org

Information on Health and Exercise

Calming Your Anxious Mind: How Mindfulness and Compassion Can Free You from Anxiety, Fear, and Panic, By Jeffrey Brantley, Forward by Jon Kabat-Zinn, New Harbinger Publications, 1993.

Eight Weeks To Optimum Health, A Proven Program For Taking Full Advantage of Your Body's Natural Healing Power, By Andrew Weil, M.D., Alfred A. Knopf, 2006.

Health Psychology, Vol. 24, No. 3, pages 297–306, Sheldon Cohen, Ph.D., Carnegie Mellon University

Healthy Aging, A Lifelong Guide To Your Physical And Spiritual Well-Being, By Andrew Weil, M.D., Alfred A. Knopf, 2005.

Health, United States, 2006, With Chartbook on Trends in the Health of Americans, U.S. Department of Health and Human Services, 2006

Health, United States, 2007, With Chartbook on Trends in the Health of Americans, U.S. Department of Health and Human Services, 2007

Natural Health, Natural Medicine, A Comprehensive Manual For Wellness and Self-Care, By Andrew Weil, M.D., Houghton Mifflin Company, 2004.

The Okinawa Program: How the World's Longest-Lived People Achieve Everlasting Health—And How You Can Too, By Bradley J. Willcox, D. Craig Willcox, and Makoto Suzuki, Three Rivers Press, 2002

The Triple Whammy Cure, by David Edelberg, M.D., with Heidi Hough. Free Press, 2006.

The Wisdom of Wilderness, Experiencing the Healing Power of Nature, By Gerald G. May, HarperCollins, 2006

Walk Away the Pounds, The Breakthrough Six-Week Program That Helps You Burn Fat, Tone Muscle, and Feel Great Without Dieting, By Leslie Sansone with Rowan Jacobsen, Warner Books, 2005.

YOU: The Owners Manual, by Michael F. Roizen, M.D. and Mehmet C. Oz, M.D., HarperCollins, 2005

WEBSITES:

American Heart Association—www.americanheart.org

Associated Bodywork & Massage Professionals—www.massagetherapy.com

Dr. Andrew Weil Website—www.drweil.com

Gardening Nude—www.gardeningnude.com

Google's Corporate Doctor blog spot—http://dr-razavi.blogspot.com

Greg Christian's Organic School Project—http://organicschoolproject.org

Health, United States, 2006, Chartbook on Trends in the Health of Americans—www.cdc.gov/nchs/data/hus/hus06.pdf

Health, United States, 2007, Chartbook on Trends in the Health of Americans—http://www.cdc.gov/nchs/data/hus/hus07.pdf

Hope In Bloom—www.hopeinbloom.org

Leave No Child Inside—a Chicago Wilderness campaign—www.kidsoutside.info

National Heart Lung and Blood Institute—www.nhlbi.nih.gov

The National Cancer Institute—www.cancer.gov

The Triple Whammy Cure Website—www.triplewhammycure.com

Therapeutic Landscapes Database website—www.healinglandscapes.org

Women's Health—www.womenshealth.gov

Information on Nutrition and Buying Food Locally

Closing the Food Gap: Resetting the Table in the Land of Plenty, by Mark Winne, Beacon Press, 2008

WEBSITES:

Buying Local—www.slowfoodusa.org

Buying Local—www.foodroutes.org

Buying Local—www.buylocalday.org

Food Cooperative Information—www.ncga.coop

Greg Christian's Organic School Project—http://organicschoolproject.org

Information on Stress, Emotions, Depression and Anxiety

On Becoming a Person, by Carl Rogers, Ph.D., Constable; New Edition, 2004

The Evolving Self, by Mihaly Csikszentmihalyi, Harper Perennial, 1994

The Price of Privilege: How Parental Pressure and Material Advantage Are Creating a Generation of Disconnected and Unhappy Kids, by Madeline Levine, Ph.D., HarperCollins, 2006

Undoing Perpetual Stress, The Missing Connection Between Depression, Anxiety, and 21st Century Illness, by Richard O'Connor. Berkley Books, 2005

Undoing Depression: What Therapy Can't Teach You and Medication Can't Give You, by Richard O'Connor. Berkley Books, 1999

How To Contact Doctors and Other Experts Referenced In This Book:

Al Gore
Honorable Al Gore
2100 West End Avenue, Suite 260
Nashville, TN 37203
615-327-2227

America In Bloom
2130 Stella Court
Columbus, OH 43215-1033
614-487-1117
www.americainbloom.org

Andrew Weil, M.D.
www.drweil.com

David Edelberg, M.D.
Author of The Triple Whammy Cure
Whole Health Chicago
2522 North Lincoln Avenue
Chicago, IL 60614
773-296-1131
www.triplewhammycure.com

David Orr, Ph.D.
Paul Sears Distinguished Professor of Environmental Studies and Politics
Oberlin College
AJ Lewis Center 210
Oberlin College, OH 44074
440-775-8121

Dino Delicata, M.D.
Otolaryngology and Surgeon
1034 Warren Avenue
Downers Grove, IL 60515
630-960-5310

Greg Christian
Chicago's Conscious Caterer
1103 West Grand Avenue
Chicago, IL 60622
312.666.4466
GregChristian.com
GetMeGregs.com
GregChristianOrganics.com
OrganicSchoolProject.org

Jim Kleinwachter
Land Protection Specialist and Conservation @ Home Program Manager
The Conservation Foundation
630-553-0687 x 302
www.theconservationfoundation.org

Kay McKeen
S.C.A.R.C.E. (School and Community Assistance for Recycling & Composting Education)
799 Roosevelt Road
Building 2, Suite 108
Glen Ellyn, IL 60137
630-545-9710
www.bookrescue.org

Kimberly Stillwell, CMT
Navitus Massage
28379 Davis Parkway
Suite 803
Warrenville, IL 60555
630-551-6300
www.navitusmassage.com

Larry Brilliant, M.D.
Google.org Executive Director
1600 Amphitheatre Parkway
Mountain View, CA 94043
www.google.org

Mihaly Csikszentmihalyi, Ph.D.
Director of the Quality of Life
Research Center
and Professor of Psychology
Claremont Graduate University
1227 N. Dartmouth Avenue
Claremont, CA 91711

**Naomi Sachs, ASLA,
Founder/Executive Director**
Therapeutic Landscapes Resource
Center, Inc.
www.healinglandscapes.org
Principal, Naomi Sachs Design
www.naomisachsdesign.com
55 South Brett Street
Beacon, NY 12508
845-831-1906

Nirmala Arora, M.D.
Suburban Center of Allergy
Advocate Good Samaritan Hospital
Tower 2 Suite 301
3825 Highland Ave
Downers Grove, IL 60515
630-769-1122

Reid Ewing, Ph.D.
Research Professor
University of Maryland
National Center for Smart Growth
Research & Education
1112J Preinkert Field House
College Park, MD 20742

Richard Louv, Ph.D.
Author of *Last Child In The Woods:
Saving Our Children From Nature-
Deficit Disorder*
www.richardlouv.com

Richard O'Connor, Ph.D.
Author of Undoing Perpetual Stress
162 West 56th Street, Suite 403
New York, New York 10019
212-977-4686

Roger Ulrich, Ph.D.
Director of the Center for Health
Systems and Design
Texas A&M University
College Station, Texas 78743-3137
979-845-7009

Simon N. Young, Ph.D.
Department of Psychiatry
McGill University
1033 Pine Ave. W.
Montreal QC H3A 1A1

Taraneh Razavi, M.D.
Corporate Doctor, Google
1600 Amphitheatre Parkway
Mountain View, CA 94043
Dr. Razavi's Good To Know Info
Blog—http://dr-razavi.blogspot.com

Vipal K. Arora, M.D., S.C.
Suburban Center of Pelviscopy
Endoscopy
Specializes in Women's Health
Concerns
Advocate Good Samaritan Hospital
Professional Building Tower 1,
Suite 5J
3825 Highland Avenue
Downers Grove, IL 60515
630-968-1100

References

Associated Bodywork & Massage Professionals. *"The Benefits of Massage."* Associated Bodywork & Massage Professionals. http://www.massagetherapy.com/learnmore/benefits.php (accessed February 27, 2008).

Batmanghelidj, M.D., F. *You're Not Sick, You're Thirsty!*. New York: Warner Books, 2003.

Bush, President George. "President Calls for Conservation and Stewardship on Earth Day, Remarks From The President On Earth Day." *Whitehouse Press Release Website.* Office of the Press Secretary. www.whitehouse.gov/news/releases/2002/04/20020422-1.html, (accessed February 27, 2008)

Cimprich, B., "Development of an intervention to restore attention in cancer patients." *Cancer Nursing* (1993) 16, 83-92.

City of Warrenville, Illinois, Permeable Paver Information. City of Warrenville, Illinois, January 2008 Press Release. http://www.warrenville.il.us/includes/uploads/File/WarrenvilleRdPermeablePavers.pdf

Climate Savers Corporate Website. "About Page." http://www.climatesaverscomputing.org/about/ (accessed July 9, 2008)

Clinton, Bill. *Giving.* New York: Alfred A. Knopf, 2007.

Cohen, Sheldon, Ph.D., *Health Psychology,* (2005) Vol. 24, No. 3, pages 297–306.

Coley, R.L., Kuo, Frances E., Sullivan, William C., "Where does community grow? The social context created by nature in urban public housing." *Environment & Behavior,* (1997) 29, 468-492.

Coronado, Shawna L., "#45—Environmental Health, You Can Change The World One Step At A Time." *The Casual Gardener Newspaper Column.* Casual Gardener Media. http://www.thecasualgardener.com/Column/Article45.html (accessed February 27, 2008).

Csikszentmihalyi, Mihaly. *The Evolving Self.* New York: Harper Perennial, 1994.

Diehm, Wm., J., "Dealing With Loneliness." *Seniors-Site.* Writers Consortium. http://seniors-site.com/widowm/lonely.html (accessed February 27, 2008).

Edelberg, David, M.D., with Hough, Heidi. *The Triple Whammy Cure.* New York: Free Press, 2006.

EPA Website, "Naled For Mosquito Control", *U.S. EPA Office of Pesticide Programs Prevention, Pesticides, and Toxic Substances Website,* http://www.epa.gov/pesticides/health/mosquitoes/naled4mosquitoes.htm, (accessed February 27, 2008)

Ewing, R. and Schmid, T., Killingsworth, R., Zlot, A., Raudenbush, S.. "Relationship between urban sprawl and physical activity, obesity, and morbidity", *American Journal of Health Promotion,* (2003) 18-1: 47-57

Faber Taylor, A., Kuo, F.E., & Sullivan, W.C., "Views of Nature and Self-Discipline: Evidence from Inner City Children." *Journal of Environmental Psychology,* (2002) 22, 49-63

Fields, Wayne. *What the River Knows, An Angler In Midstream.* Chicago: University of Chicago Press, 1996.

Fortune Magazine. "100 Best Companies To Work For." *Money.CNN.Com Fortune 100 Best Companies To Work For.* Money.CNN.Com. http://money.cnn.com/magazines/fortune/bestcompanies/2008/full_list (accessed August 31, 2008).

Fox, Maggie. "Allergies cost Americans $11 billion: survey." *Yahoo News Website.* http://news.yahoo.com/s/nm/20080611/hl_nm/allergis_usa_dc (accessed June 12, 2008).

Goodall, Jane & Bekoff, Marc. *The Ten Trusts, What We Must Do To Care For The Animals We Love.* New York: HarperCollins, 2002.

Google Corporate Website. "At Google, we're committed to helping build a clean energy future." http://www.google.com/corporate/green/energy (accessed July 9, 2008)

Google Doctor Blog. "Dr. Razavi's Good to Know Info." http://dr-razavi.blogspot.com (accessed July 12, 2008)

Google's Official Blog. "Get Outdoors With GO Georgia." http://googleblog.blogspot.com/2008/06/get-outdoors-with-go-georgia.html (accessed July 10, 2008)

Gore, Al. *An Inconvenient Truth, The Planetary Emergency Of Global Warming And What We Can Do About It.* Pennsylvania: Rodale, 2006.

Hartig, T., Mang, M., Evans, G.W. "Restorative effects of natural environment experiences." *Environment & Behavior,* (1991). 23, 3-26.

Hill, Julia Butterfly. *The Legacy of Luna, The Story Of A Tree, A Woman, and The Struggle To Save The Redwoods.* New York: HarperCollins, 2000.

Kaplan, R. "Wilderness perception and psychological benefits: An analysis of a continuing program." *Leisure Sciences,* (1984), 6, 271-290.

Klaassen, Curtis D., and Liu, Jie, "Induction of Mettallothionein as an Adaptive Mechanism Affecting the Magnitude and Progression of Toxicological Injury," *Toxicological Defense Mechanisms and the Shape of Dose-Response Relationships Environmental Health Perspectives,* (1998) 106, Supplement 1, February.

Kuo, Frances E. and Sullivan, William C., Aggression and violence in the inner city: Impacts of environment via mental fatigue. *Environment & Behavior,* (2001) 33(4), 543-571.

Kuo, Frances E. and Sullivan, William C., "Environment and crime in the inner city: Does vegetation reduce crime?" *Environment and Behavior,* (2001) 33(3), 343-367.

Kuo, Frances E. and Sullivan, William C., Coley, R.L., & Brunson, L. Fertile ground for community: Inner-city neighborhood common spaces. *American Journal of Community Psychology,* (1998) 26(6), 823-851.

La Monica, Paul R. "Google leaders stick with $1 salary." *CNN Money.* CNN Money.com. http://money.cnn.com/2006/03/31/technology/google/index.htm. (accessed June 17, 2008)

Levine, Madeline, Ph.D. *The Price of Privilege: How Parental Pressure and Material Advantage Are Creating a Generation of Disconnected and Unhappy Kids.* New York: HarperCollins, 2006.

Lewis, Jone Johnson. "Grandma Moses Quotes." *About.Com: Womens History.* About.Com. http://womenshistory.about.com/library/qu/blqumose.htm (accessed February 27, 2008).

Lewis, Jone Johnson. "Pearl S. Buck Quotes". *About.Com: Womens History.* About.Com. http://womenshistory.about.com/od/quotes/a/pearl_buck.htm (accessed February 27, 2008).

Lohr, V.I., Pearson-Mimms, C.H., Goodwin, G.K. "Interior plants may improve worker productivity and reduce stress in a windowless environment." *Journal of Environmental Horticulture,* (1996), 14, 97-100.

Louv, Richard. *Last Child In The Woods: Saving Our Children From Nature-Deficit Disorder.* Algonquin Books, 2008.

Lovelock, James. *The Revenge of Gaia, Earth's Climate Crisis & The Fate Of Humanity.* New York: Basic Books, 2006.

May, Gerald G. *The Wisdom of Wilderness, Experiencing the Healing Power of Nature.* New York: HarperCollins, 2006.

McKay, Kim and Bonnin, Jenny. *True Green, 100 Everyday Ways You Can Contribute To A Healthier Planet.* Washington, D.C.: National Geographic, 2006.

Mehl, A. et al. "The effect of trichlorfon and other organophosphates on prenatal brain development in the guinea pig." *Neurochem. Res.* (1994)19:569-574.

Miles, I., Sullivan, W.C., Kuo, F.E. "Prairie restoration volunteers: The benefits of participation. *Urban Ecosystems,* (1998) 2, 27-41.

Orr, David, Ph.D. *Earth in Mind: On Education, Environment, and the Human Prospect.* Washington, D.C.: Island Press, 2004.

Nelson, Senator Gaylord. "How the First Earth Day Came About." *Envirolink Website.* http://earthday.envirolink.org/history.html (accessed February 27, 2008).

New York State. "Information Sheet: Malathion and Mosquito Control." *Department of Health, Diseases & Conditions—West Nile Virus.* New York Department of Health. http://www.health.state.ny.us/nysdoh/westnile/education/2740.htm (accessed February 27, 2008).

Reigart, J.R. and J.R. Roberts. "Recognition and management of pesticide poisonings." *U.S. EPA Office of Pesticide Health & Safety, National Strategies for Healthcare Providers.* U.S. EPA. http://www.epa.gov/oppfead1/safety/healthcare/handbook/handbook.htm (accessed February 27, 2008).

Rogers, Ph.D., Carl. *On Becoming a Person.* Constable; New Edition, 2004

Roizen, Michael F., M.D., and Mehmet C. Oz, M.D. *YOU: The Owners Manual.* New York: HarperCollins 2005.

Sansone, Leslie with Jacobsen, Rowan. *Walk Away the Pounds, The Breakthrough Six-Week Program That Helps You Burn Fat, Tone Muscle, and Feel Great Without Dieting.* New York: Warner Books, 2005.

Sarin, S. and K.D. Gill. "Biochemical and behavioral deficits in adult rat following chronic dichlorvos exposure", *Pharmacologic Biochemical Behavior,* (1998), 59: 1081-1086.

Sarin, S. and K.D. Gill, "Dichlorvos induced alterations in glucose homeostasis: Possible implications on the state of neuronal function in rats. Mol. Cell." *Biochem.* (1999) 199:97-92.

TED Ideas Worth Spreading, "Speakers; Dr. Larry Brilliant, Epidemiologist, Philanthropist."http://www.ted.com/index.php/speakers/larry_brilliant.html (Accessed July 12, 2008).

TED Ideas Worth Spreading, "About TED." http://www.ted.com/index.php/pages/view/id/5 (Accessed July 12, 2008)

Tennessen, C., Cimprich, B. "Views to nature: Effects on attention", *Journal of Environmental Psychology,* (1995), 15: 77-85.

Teresa, Mother. *Mother Teresa: In My Own Words.* Gramercy,1997.

Twain, Mark. "Directory of Mark Twain's maxims, quotations, and various opinions." Twainquotes. http://www.twainquotes.com/Right.html (accessed February 27, 2008).

Time Inc. Health. *Dr. Koop's Self-Care Advisor.* Time Inc. Health, 1996.

United Nations Environment Programme. *Taking Action, An Environmental Guide For You and Your Community.* Hong Kong: Colorcraft, 1995.

U.S. Department of Health and Human Services, *Health, United States, 2006, With Chartbook on Trends in the Health of Americans,* 2006.

U.S. Department of Health and Human Services, *Health, United States, 2007, With Chartbook on Trends in the Health of Americans,* 2007.

U.S. EPA. "Pesticide Reregistration Eligibility Decision for Naled." *U.S. EPA Office of Pesticide Programs Prevention, Pesticides, and Toxic Substances Website.* http://www.epa.gov/pesticides/reregistration/REDs/naled_red.pdf (accessed February 27, 2008).

U.S. EPA. "Pesticide Reregistration Eligibility Decision for Malathion." *U.S. EPA Office of Pesticide Programs Prevention, Pesticides, and Toxic Substances Website.* http://www.epa.gov/pesticides/reregistration/REDs/malathion_red.pdf (accessed February 27, 2008).

U.S. EPA. "Pesticide Reregistration Status for Organophosphates". *U.S. EPA Office of Pesticide Programs Prevention, Pesticides, and Toxic Substances Website.* http://www.epa.gov/pesticides/reregistration/status_op.htm (accessed February 27, 2008).

UT Southwestern Medical Center. (2006, October 23). "New Asthma Medicine Targets Vulnerable Inner-city Children". *ScienceDaily.* http://www.sciencedaily.com/releases/2006/10/061019093700.htm (accessed February 27, 2008).

Weil, Andrew, M.D. *Eight Weeks To Optimum Health, A Proven Program For Taking Full Advantage of Your Body's Natural Healing Power.* New York: Alfred A. Knopf, 2006.

Weil, Andrew, M.D. *Healthy Aging, A Lifelong Guide To Your Physical And Spiritual Well-Being.* New York: Alfred A. Knopf, 2005.

Weil, Andrew, M.D. *Natural Health, Natural Medicine, A Comprehensive Manual For Wellness and Self-Care.* Boston: Houghton Mifflin Company, 2004.

Willcox, Bradley J, D. Craig Willcox, and Makoto Suzuki. *The Okinawa Program: How the World's Longest-Lived People Achieve Everlasting Health—And How You Can Too.* New York: Three Rivers Press, 2002.

Young, Dick. *Kane County Wild Plants & Natural Areas.* Geneva, Illinois: Kane County, 1986.

Young, Simon N., "How to increase serotonin in the human brain without drugs." *Journal of Psychiatry and Neuroscience* (2007); 32(6): 394-399

Index

Something Fun:
Secret Messages Are Hidden
In This Book!

Be at one with yourself and Shawna's greening and gardening buddy, Harry the Pug. There is one message which is hidden within the chapter text of this book. Find the message for some fun inspiration. The clue to find the primary hidden message is on the cover of this book.

Additional inspirational messages can be found on the cover pages for the various "parts" of *Gardening Nude*; use the front page clue to further guide you in solving them.

According to the Tao of Harry the Pug, "Be at peace with yourself and the world. Find your inner woof by reading the book and let the hidden messages inspire you."

About the Author

Shawna Lee Coronado is an author, locally syndicated newspaper columnist, energetic speaker, and environmental and health correspondent with over eighteen years of experience with sales and public relations.

Being very active in local community is critical to Shawna's inspirational message. She is heavily involved with many community greening and improvement organizations and is currently on the Board of Directors for Fermilab National Accelerators Natural Areas. She works closely with the local America In Bloom organization and has participated in many local groups such as environmental advisory commissions, parks and forestry associations, and educational institutions.

Shawna's experience in business development, communication, sales management, and online marketing has helped her spread the positive health and greening message. Shawna's goal is to inspire the world, with her dynamic personality and infectious enthusiasm, to get off the couch and get out into the environment and community to improve physical and emotional health!

Focused on nature, Shawna's landscape design and gardening expertise motivates her to be outdoors experiencing a healthier lifestyle. You can find Shawna staying healthy by working regularly in her garden with the family dog and mascot, Harry the Pug.

Shawna's feisty personality and passion about health, greening the environment, and building community makes her an inspiring choice as a public speaker. To contact Shawna regarding appearances, please visit either of her corporate websites; www.thecasualgardener.com and www.gardeningnude.com.

For information regarding special discounts for bulk purchases of *Gardening Nude* for either retail sale or motivational/educational purposes, please contact The Casual Gardener Company at www.thecasualgardener.com.